SHARK
ATTACK

VICTOR COPPLESON AND PETER GOADBY

SHARK ATTACK

HOW, WHY, WHEN & WHERE SHARKS ATTACK HUMANS

ANGUS
& ROBERTSON
PUBLISHERS

*Cover photographs: Colour photographs
by Ron and Valerie Taylor;
black and white photograph
by kind permission of*
The Sunday Telegraph.

ANGUS & ROBERTSON PUBLISHERS

*Unit 4, Eden Park, 31 Waterloo Road,
North Ryde, NSW, Australia 2113, and
16 Golden Square, London W1R 4BN,
United Kingdom*

*This book is copyright.
Apart from any fair dealing for the
purposes of private study, research,
criticism or review, as permitted
under the Copyright Act, no part may
be reproduced by any process without
written permission. Inquiries should
be addressed to the publishers.*

*First published by Angus & Robertson Publishers in 1958
Revised edition 1962
First paperback edition (as* Killer Sharks*) 1968
Revised editions 1976, 1982
This revised edition 1988*

*Copyright © 1958 by E. Niesche
Copyright © revisions 1968, 1976, 1988 by Peter Goadby*

ISBN 0 207 15350 7

*Typeset in 11pt Baskerville by Setrite Typesetters
Printed in Australia by Australian Print Group*

CONTENTS

Foreword

FOREWORD

This latest edition of the late Sir Victor Coppleson's famous book *Shark Attack* has been revised and amplified to include new information, published and unpublished, from scientists, divers and fishermen, and the results of continuing experience and study. This edition reflects not only our increased knowledge but also changes in ecological conditions and in human habits as more people spend more time on and in the cool waters that are the environment of the great white shark.

Sir Victor's theories expressed in the first edition of this book back in 1958 have been the basis of much research right around the world. Whenever a pioneer has the courage to set out and attempt to interpret the available knowledge on a previously unresearched subject, it is to be expected that subsequent research and analysis may put different connotations on some of the data he or she has collected. In the light of further research some of Coppleson's original hypotheses and theories can be read to give different answers, yet continuing analysis and recent happenings still lend weight to the theories that were set out so long ago and have triggered so much work.

But we are seeing changes in the pattern of shark attacks. Increasing use of wetsuits, board surfing, increased leisure time and even the conservation of seals and sea lions are factors that have led to a change in the ratio of attacks by warm water species to attacks by the white shark of temperate waters.

It is difficult to be involved with sharks without feeling a natural repugnance at the thought of being chewed, chopped or eaten, particularly in an unfamiliar environment. In spite of this repugnance, however, there is a fascination with and strong interest in these great and ancient animals.

With improvements in modern communication, areas where attacks were unreported are now in the public eye. It seems incredible, but afternoon newspapers in many of the world's great cities will still devote the first three pages of an edition to reporting an attack and summarising previous history. Such a high level of public interest will ensure that knowledge increases further and that we continue to search for better ways of protecting ourselves from shark attacks. Sharks are powerful and dangerous animals that should never be treated casually. In attacking, they are doing the job for which they have evolved.

Peter Goadby
Sydney, 1987

PART I

THE SHARK
IN ACTION

THE MAN-KILLERS

Sharks originated in the Devonian period some 350 million years ago, and many species seem to have changed little through evolution. Like their ancestors that inhabited the earth's turbulent waters long before the human species evolved, modern sharks still have skeletons of cartilage, pointed snouts, and mouths on the underside of their heads.

Many sharks are large and fearsome. In fact, one whale-like but harmless variety grows to about 18 metres. But there are others, such as the pygmy shark, that measure only 20 centimetres or so when fully matured.

Throughout this book, and indeed through recorded history, there are numerous reports of humans being attacked by sharks in the water — and even out of the water. In most cases, either the victim recognised the attacker as a shark or onlookers saw one in the process of attacking, while in those instances where strict proof is lacking, there has usually been strong circumstantial evidence that a shark was responsible.

But apart from the evidence of eye-witnesses and victims, irrefutable scientific evidence of a shark's guilt is often provided. The discovery of shark's teeth in wounds, or finding missing portions of a victim in a shark's stomach, at times makes it possible to determine the actual species of shark responsible. In an attack off Rey Island in the Gulf of Panama in 1944, for instance, parts of two teeth found in the wound of a sailor by the surgeon who operated on him proved conclusively that a shark — the great white shark (*Carcharodon carcharias*) — was responsible for his injuries.

Other evidence of the responsibility of sharks for the majority of these attacks is overwhelming. In Australia and many other parts of the world, the menace is taken so seriously that practically all ocean beaches where numbers of people bathe are equipped with lookout towers to spot sharks and warn bathers of their presence. Often, during the summer months, the shark warning bell clangs and it is remarkable how quickly a large section of surf can be emptied of thousands of bathers. Helicopters and fixed wing aircraft are also helpful in spotting sharks, although there is evidence that the thumping of hovering helicopter blades can attract sharks or trigger action.

Of the 361 shark species listed by FAO (Food and Agriculture Organisation of the United Nations), the white shark, the tiger shark and the big carcharhinid (whaler) species are regular man-killers and attackers. Blue sharks, makos, hammerheads, and other big carcharhinids are also acknowledged human attackers. These are the species that because of their size, power and mouth size are consistently dangerous.

Other shark species and families may occasionally damage humans and boats. Garrick and Shultz, in their paper on potentially dangerous sharks, listed the species that have attacked humans, sometimes fatally, and damaged boats. Some of the species are listed as rarely attacking, or attacking only in exceptional circumstances or under provocation. The list of human attackers is dominated by three shark species — white sharks, tiger sharks and the bull shark whaler, *C. leucas.*

The most ferocious is probably the great white shark or white pointer. This shark moves swiftly through the water and has rows of large triangular teeth. It is a shark which sometimes follows ships, trailing them for long distances. Undoubtedly it is a man-killer. Of the great white shark, Jonathan Couch, in his *History of the Fishes of the British Isles*, wrote: "It is to sailors the most formidable of all the inhabitants of the sea, for in none besides are the powers of inflicting injury so equally combined with eagerness to accomplish it."

It has long been regarded as dangerous. Pennant, describing the white shark in 1776, wrote:

This grows to a very great bulk. Gillius says that in the belly of one was found a human corpse entire, which is far from incredible, considering their vast greediness after human flesh. They are the dread of the sailors in all hot climates, where they constantly attend the ships in expectation of what may drop overboard. A man that has this misfortune perishes without redemption. They have been seen to dart at him like gudgeons to a worm... Swimmers very often perish by them.

One of the first recorded drawings of a shark attack appeared in Olaus Magnus's
Historia de Gentibus Septentrionalibus *in* Icones Animalium.
AUSTRALIAN MUSEUM LIBRARY

*Sometimes they lost an arm or a leg and sometimes were bit
quite asunder, serving but for two morsels for this ravenous
animal.*

Others reported finding a body in armour, and according to
one account, a whole horse inside this monster.

Although the number of shark attacks generally is decreasing,
attacks by the white shark or, as it is sometimes called, the "white
death", continue to take their savage toll. Wetsuits give surfers
and skindivers insulation against the biting cold of the lower
temperature water but not against the savagely biting teeth of
a hungry white shark. As the area of human sporting activity
in the sea extends into the lower temperature water, so are the
chances of meeting the white shark face to face increased. The
fatal attacks on swimmer Leslie Jordan, lifesaver William Black,
and spearfisherman Graham Hitt, off Dunedin, New Zealand,
show the savagery and spread of the ferocious white sharks. The
white shark attacks in cool water are a constant reminder that
sharks and danger are possible seawater companions everywhere.

Off California and Oregon, USA, Robert Lee and Daniel
Miller listed 34 attacks between 20 July 1969 and 30 September
1984. Of these all but three were attacks by white sharks.

In Australia, the white shark has been responsible for
numerous attacks in southern waters.

Another dangerous genus is *Carcharhinus* (the whalers).
Dr J. A. F. Garrick considers that there are 25 species of
Carcharhinus. His opinion is that 14 of these may logically,

because of size, environment and aggressiveness, be regarded as potentially dangerous to humans. The other 11 species would also be dangerous were it not for the relatively small size to which they grow. Dr Garrick's paper shows that the dangerous bull shark (*C. leucas*) is the species which has caused attacks and fatalities in Lake Nicaragua and South Africa as well as Australia. This species is at home in the fresh and brackish water of rivers and lakes as well as in the salt water of the open sea.

Three other *Carcharhinus* are dangerous to open ocean and estuary swimmers. *Carcharhinus amboinensis* (pigeye shark) frequents fresh and brackish water, and *C. obscurus* (dusky shark) and *C. brachyurus* (copper shark) are also dangerous to swimmers both on ocean beaches and inshore in estuaries.

Stewart Springer names the white-tipped shark (*C. longimanus*) as one of the most voracious, aggressive and dangerous open sea sharks in United States waters.

In tropical coral reef waters *C. albimarginatus* (silvertip shark) and *C. amblyrhynchos* (grey reef shark) sometimes exhibit aggression towards divers and could be a problem to swimmers around coral reefs.

Carcharhinus species were for many years the great scourge of the crowds at the bathing ghats at Calcutta. Sir Joseph Fayrer says the sharks used to feed on the partially burnt bodies thrown into the river from the funeral ghats. When this custom was discontinued, the sharks began attacking the people near the ghats, especially in April and May, when the river is very salty.

Sir Joseph stated that the sharks would dash into the crowd at the ghat and inflict dangerous and, at times, mortal wounds, although they seldom succeeded in carrying off their prey because of the many people bathing.

The tiger shark, *Galeocerdo cuvier*, another dangerous species, receives its name from tiger-like stripes which are clearly distinguishable in its young, but are less definite in older sharks. It grows to 5 metres and is widely distributed in temperate and tropical waters. The tiger also frequents harbours and estuaries. It has been blamed mostly for attacks on open sea beaches and in offshore waters.

Other sharks regarded with suspicion or which have had attacks attributed to them include the lemon shark (*Negaprion brevirostris*), the mako shark (*Isurus oxyrinchus*) and its close relative the porbeagle shark (*Lamna nasus*), the hammerheads (*Sphyrna* spp.), the blue shark (*Prionace glauca*), and the black-tipped sharks (*Carcharhinus brevipinna, C. limbatus*).

The mako, sometimes known as the blue pointer, is an open sea shark. As a big game fish, it has a reputation for tenacity and spectacular fighting. There is no evidence yet to incriminate it as a man-killer, but it does attack boats.

The grey nurse (*Engomphodus taurus*) was once thought to be a man-eater, but this is no longer believed to be true. The long, thin teeth certainly give it an evil, voracious appearance. The grey nurse is a reef dweller and is sluggish and slow-moving in its daytime habits. Grey nurses hang in the gutters and crevasses of the submerged reefs in schools and remain almost motionless, head turned towards the current. They fall easy prey to spearfishermen with "smokies" (powerheads). Grey nurses move with school fishes such as mullet, tailor, or salmon, on their migrations along the coast.

In the coastal waters of New South Wales, Australia, where it once held its sinister reputation, the grey nurse and its close relative the deepwater Herbst are now protected species. The capture of the grey nurse in South Africa is highest at the time of the lowest incidence of South African shark attacks, so here, too, is further support for the present-day theory that the grey nurse is no more dangerous than the wobbegong or carpet shark which spends its daytime hours lying doggo on the weedy reef bottom. The teeth of the grey nurse are designed to grab and hold fish; they are too fragile and delicate in section to be used in attacks on mammals, and to hold, tear and worry flesh free from a large body. The grey nurse is not built for high speed activity over long distances; it remains almost immobile after being hooked on rod and reel. This is demonstrated by the regular weighing-in of specimens of 100 kilograms and more on lines tested at only 10 or even 6 kilograms. It is difficult to distinguish between the fight put up by the slothful wobbegong and the grey nurse.

Many authorities, especially in the United States, regard the hammerhead sharks (*Sphyrna* spp.) as man-killers. The hammerhead shark is common in the open sea and is remarkable for its flattened hammer-shaped head, with eyes at the extremity. It has a small curved mouth on the underside of its head.

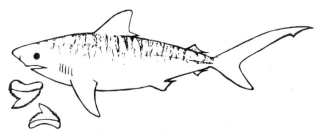

(i) tiger shark (Galeocerdo cuvier);

(ii) white shark (Carcharodon carcharias);

(iii) bull shark (Carcharinus leucas);

(iv) blue shark (Prionace glauca);

(v) shortfin mako (Isurus oxyrinchus);

(vi) smooth hammerhead (Sphyrna zygaena);

(vii) dusky shark (Carcharinus obscuras);

(viii) copper shark (Carcharinus brachyurus).

The olfactory canal of a hammerhead runs along the leading edge of the head.
PETER GOADBY

Hammerheads are sometimes shy and difficult to entice to take baits, but at other times they are pugnacious — especially pregnant females — and will even grab pieces of paper, the chum pot or the game boat itself, when excited by the scent of bait or berley in the water. The hammerhead is the "marine blood-hound", able to follow the scent of even a single bait fish for miles before deciding to strike. As befits its competitive open water life the hammerhead, of which there are at least three species in Australian waters, fights actively and can swim very fast. Hammerheads have good eyesight and can sometimes be frightened by a sharp arm movement.

Large varieties of this shark are found on the east and west coasts of the United States, where they have been credited with a number of attacks. There has, however, been little evidence to implicate the smaller varieties found in Australia and other parts of the world in attacks on humans.

The blue shark is regarded as a man-killer in some parts of the Atlantic Ocean and Mediterranean Sea where it is reported to grow up to 4.6 metres in length, but along the coast of

California, where it is the commonest shark, it is regarded as usually harmless. Its brilliant blue back and snow-white belly make this shark one of the most conspicuous and easily identifiable of all sharks. Despite its lazy swimming appearance, slim build and poor fighting qualities, the blue shark is well equipped with strong purposeful teeth and is capable of "scooping out" meat and blubber in its attacks on whales and dolphin.

Other large sharks are regarded with suspicion. There is also good reason to believe that a number of species of sharks ordinarily docile, will at times attack man, if provoked, or especially if the men are holding fish.

The thresher sharks (*Alopias* spp.), which have a tail as long as the body, are not regarded as being dangerous to man. The harmless basking shark (*Cetorhinus maximus*) and the whale shark (*Rhiniodon typus*) are only occasionally seen in Australian waters.

New species of sharks are still being discovered and identified. One of the most interesting is the big megamouth *Megachasma pelagios*. The first specimen, measuring 4.5 metres and weighing 750 kilograms, was entangled in equipment being raised from the ocean depths off Hawaii in 1976. This unusual plankton-eating shark with luminescence throughout its mouth had never

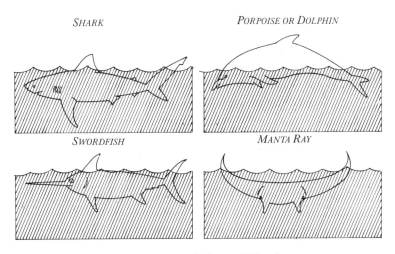

Fins of shark, porpoise or dolphin, swordfish and manta ray.

been recorded before. In 1984 a second specimen of this rare shark, almost as big as the first, was captured off Southern California.

Sharks can be distinguished from other fishes by having five to seven gill slits on each side of the head, but it is difficult to identify shark even when they are seen swimming right on the surface. In many sea conditions it is, in fact, difficult to differentiate between the dorsal fins of shark, porpoise, dolphin, broadbill swordfish, marlin and sunfish, or the tips of the wings of big rays. Even experienced fishermen are sometimes wrong or unsure, and an expert is invariably needed to distinguish the exact species of a shark when one has been landed. Most newspaper reports that a particular type of shark was caught or involved in an attack are usually found on investigation to be based on guesswork rather than accurate or scientific knowledge. Various *Carcharhinus* species have often been erroneously given the more glamorous name grey nurse in such reports, causing the true grey nurse to acquire an unwarranted reputation as a man-killer.

Identification of the species is difficult and requires specialised knowledge, experience and the use of identification keys based on different measurements and other characteristics of the various shark species. The eyes, teeth, tails, fins, and colouration may be variable and confusing. White sharks for example can range in upper body colour from almost white to very dark grey, or even a golden brown.

Teeth are a reliable guide to identifying the various species of shark. Usually in a shark's mouth only one full row of teeth is visible, but if a dried skeleton of a jaw is examined, five or six rows can be seen lying flat against the jaw cartilage. These are unerupted teeth which come into use progressively as the front ones are replaced.

The shark's teeth are firmly implanted in the integuments but have no sockets. At times teeth found in a victim's wounds give irrefutable evidence of the guilt of the shark and provide the most positive means of identifying its species. Attacking sharks identified in this way in various parts of the world have been white sharks, tiger sharks, and the whaler species.

Most large sharks grasp their food and tear and worry the piece of flesh held in their jaws free from the rest of the body.

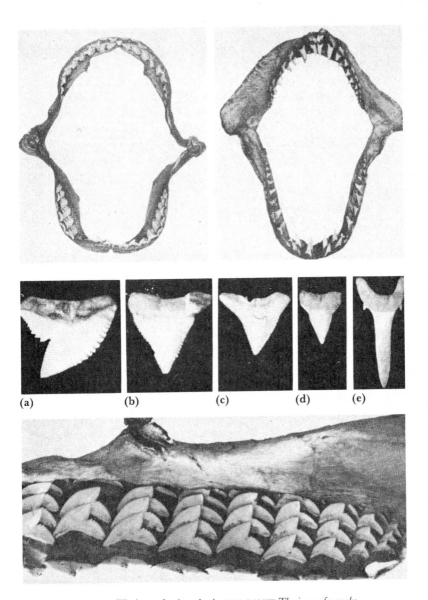

TOP LEFT: The jaws of a tiger shark. TOP-RIGHT: The jaws of a mako.

CENTRE: Isolated teeth of sharks: (a) the tiger shark; (b) the white shark; (c) the whaler, upper jaw; (d) the whaler, lower jaw; (e) the grey nurse.

BOTTOM: Portion of the dried jaws of a tiger shark with flesh removed, showing the rows of unerupted teeth.

A shark "bite meter" (gnathodynamometer) was tested by J. N. Snodgrass and Dr Perry Gilbert on tiger, lemon and dusky sharks. The test showed the maximum bite force of a dusky (whaler) shark was 60 kilograms over an area of 2 square millimetres — equivalent to 3 tonnes per square centimetre. In addition to the shearing power of the bite, sharks can break as well as cut bones during their attack on fishes or humans.

The offensive weapons of a shark, however, are not confined to its teeth. It can strike with great force with its body, cut deeply or even amputate an arm with its fins, and kick powerfully with its tail. The skin of the larger sharks must also be counted as a weapon. It is so rough that victims often show, in addition to wounds caused by the bite, long grazes on other parts of their bodies caused by the shark's impact against them. Many references are made to this type of injury. Numerous accounts will be given also of swimmers being thrown bodily into the air by the great force of a shark's rush. At times during an attack, swimmers near a victim have received severe injuries in this way as the shark brushed past them on its way to the victim. Shark's skin is extremely hard, having countless minute plates of enamel-covered dentine, known as placoid scales, each of which, in reality, is a miniature tooth. These scales are so firmly attached to the skin they are difficult to remove and so hard they will take a stonelike polish. It is therefore not surprising that a 15 centimetre incision in a shark's hide will soon burr the sharpest knife. Numerous reports mention that spears fired at close range have merely scratched the hard skin of the shark and bounced off. Others suggest that even a sharp knife is little defence. Against a large shark in its killing pattern, arms and fists are useless.

Underwater fishermen who have tried to harpoon sharks when they found themselves in tough spots have more than an academic interest in the vital and vulnerable parts of a shark's anatomy.

They have found that sharks are most difficult to kill and that great skill and accuracy are needed to plunge a spear into the small heart or brain-cage. They aim their spears for the midline at a point as far behind a shark's eyes as the snout is in front. Many experienced spearfishermen aim their harpoons through the gills, which are more accessible and as vital to a shark as lungs are to a mammal.

TOP: *The Shark Arm case. The cottage "Cored Joy".*

BOTTOM: *Portions of sharks' skin, showing denticles.*
LEFT: *Tiger shark.* RIGHT: *Wobbegong shark.*

It is even more difficult to kill a big shark with a knife. Little notice can be taken of stories that sharks can be dispatched merely by ripping them open along the belly. Too many instances are known in which sharks have been cut open, disembowelled and thrown back into the water, yet have swum about for some time. There are other stories of sharks swimming around with pickaxes in their heads and spears through their bodies. Even seriously wounded sharks have shown remarkable vitality. When not wounded in a vital spot, a shark will usually struggle against capture until it dies from loss of blood or until its mates fall on it and consume everything but the head. Some sharks have been hooked, shot full of lead from a repeating rifle, harpooned, hauled on deck and disembowelled, yet stayed alive and alert for a long time.

Powerheads are so far the most efficient weapon against sharks. They use either a 12-gauge shotgun cartridge or a .303 military rifle cartridge in an open, elongated, bell-shaped holder with the firing cap sitting on a pin ready for instant use. The cartridge holder and the firing pin are fixed on the end of a spear which, when pushed against the shark, presses the cartridge against the firing pin and explodes it.

Before the use of powerheads, Ron Taylor, Dave Rawlings and Ted Louis used a method of paralysing sharks with poisons loaded by Dr Shane Watson. Ron Taylor, an underwater photographer of the year and world spearfishing champion, now

 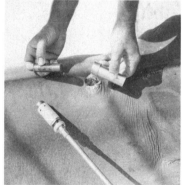

The powerhead, an efficient shark killer. RON AND VALERIE TAYLOR

combines his talents by taking underwater photographs of sharks in their natural environment and searching for means of defence against shark attack. Ron and Valerie Taylor's shark photographs and movies are sought right around the world.

After the series of experiments with the hypodermic syringes loaded with poisons, including strychnine, the world's spearfishermen found that the explosive-headed spear was the spearfisherman's best weapon against sharks. Powerheads are now in extensive use around the world and have proved their effectiveness whether loaded with shotgun or service rifle cartridges. Spearfishermen who wish to kill sharks or other big marine animals now use the powerhead that screws onto the spear shaft of a spear gun or on a separate rigid shaft. The explosive killing power is provided by the detonation on contact of a rifle or shotgun cartridge. The rigid shaft powerhead is also used from above the surface from boats when sharks are a problem to fish that are being caught commercially or recreationally. Wally Gibbins of Sydney killed a giant tiger shark of 350 kilograms at the Great Barrier Reef, and John Harding used the powerhead on a 3 metre white shark estimated to weigh 180 kilograms in northern New South Wales.

Much can also be learned about sharks and their habits from game fishermen. Game fishermen find sharks strenuous, powerful and tenacious fighters. The mako, particularly, is regarded as a tough, dangerous opponent. Makos have been known to jump straight into the air, higher than a fishing launch's mast, and occasionally into the cockpit, wrecking everything within reach.

There is reason to believe that the consistent fishing of large sharks appreciably reduces the shark population and the probability of attack, and this sport is popular in many parts of the world. Durban in South Africa, the coasts of Australia and New Zealand and the East Coast of the USA have international reputations for shark fishing. At Sydney's front door, where the American novelist Zane Grey did much to publicise shark fishing, large tiger sharks, white sharks, whalers, threshers, grey nurses, hammerheads and makos are weighed. Some of the sharks caught have weighed over 800 kilograms.

South Australia is world famous for its white pointer (white shark) fishing grounds. These waters are the home of really big white sharks over 1500 kilograms. The International Game Fish Association (IGFA) world record is 1211 kilograms on 60 kilogram line. The wonderful blend of big sharks, seals and shallow water gave unparalleled record-breaking potential in South Australia before the white shark population was dramatically reduced by commercial fishermen seeking this species for jaws and teeth.

Cape Moreton near Brisbane (Australia) offers world-class challenge with giant tigers, whites and the various whaler species. At one time the world's 60 kilogram line tiger and white shark records were both held in Brisbane.

Some valuable clues in combating sharks have been learnt from commercial fishing. It has been found that once a shark runs into or even touches a net, it is in trouble. Instead of retreating, it panics in a bull-headed attempt to force its way through. It then becomes entangled and literally drowns itself. (A shark may asphyxiate if it cannot swim.) In its efforts to break free, it often damages the net, and this is one of the great expenses of this form of shark catching.

As most of the larger sharks are more or less solitary in their habits, it is only the few species which travel in vast schools that have provided commercially successful fishing. For this reason, the most lucrative type of shark fishing has been associated with the small school shark, about 120 to 150 centimetres long. But even the once prolific school shark could not stand modern fishing pressures and the State Government Fisheries Departments in southern Australia have now enforced a statutory period of prohibition from fishing (with the approval of the Federal Government Department of Australian Fisheries Service).

Similarly, most of the companies in the shark catching business which have concentrated on the larger sharks of the man-killer types have found supplies soon exhausted in areas where at first they were plentiful. In fact, none of the attempts to exploit these sharks commercially, even in once shark-rich areas in Australia and other parts of the world, has been a financial success. Within a short period, all were fished out to an unprofitable level.

This reduction of shark population in particular areas by netting is the basis of the system of shark meshing which has so successfully eliminated fatal attacks on the Sydney and Durban beaches. Perhaps it may not have helped to balance the shark companies' books, but it has been a decided boon for bathers.

In addition to shark meshing, the world shark population is dramatically reduced by the catches of the world's long line fishermen who set from their vessels. The lines are up to 90 kilometres long and may use as many as 2000 hooks per line, which must take its toll on these ocean predators as well as on the other pelagic fish such as the tuna and marlin.

THE STRANGE
APPETITES AND
DIGESTION OF SHARKS

It is always an interesting experience to open up a large shark. Inside its stomach there is likely to be anything from a fur coat or a bottle opener to a brick or a pedigreed pup. Bottles, tins and sundry junk are often found. One shark caught in Sydney Harbour had in its stomach half a ham, several legs of mutton, the hindquarter of a pig, the head and forelegs of a bulldog with a rope tied around its neck, a quantity of horseflesh, a piece of sacking and a ship's scraper. Inside another shark, caught at Bondi, New South Wales, were a full-grown spaniel complete with collar, several seabirds, a mass of fish, a porpoise's skull and the spines of a porcupine fish. A shark caught in the Adriatic produced three overcoats, a nylon raincoat and a driver's licence.

In 1949 the late Dr E. W. Gudger, for many years ichthyologist at the American Museum of Natural History, New York, and a noted authority on the subject of sharks, made a special investigation in Florida of their digestion. He studied chiefly the tiger shark, the largest, hungriest and fiercest of its genus, and found that its jaws and teeth chop its prey into large fragments which are swallowed whole.

The teeth lie parallel with the mouth and only come upright as the jaws open wide. In taking small food, the teeth need not be used if the prey size allows it to be swallowed in one piece. Feeding on big fish and mammals necessitates the tearing of chunks from the animal. The teeth of the upper jaw are driven into the flesh and then those of the lower jaw are inserted with the jaw closure. The shark will then relax its body to hang in the water and allow its body weight and head shaking to tear a chunk from its prey. (A pet theory about sharks, which is not strictly true, is that they must turn on their sides to bite. This was first propounded by the Roman historian, Pliny.)

The attack position with jaw protruding, nose lifted and teeth pulled upright. At close quarters, the eye is often rolled back, or if the shark has a nictitating membrane, this will slide across the eye.

Dr Gudger caught his tigers near a slaughterhouse. The stomach of one shark contained the skull of a horse with some vertebrae attached, two hoofs, several green turtle scutes (bony plates), parts of several large conch shells and a piece of tile.

In another tiger he found a washtub full of yellow liquid. From this he picked fish bones, grass, feathers, bones of marine birds, fragments of turtle shell, old cans, a dozen vertebrae and the skull of a cow minus its horns. The flesh of the cow's head had been partly digested and the skull partially dissolved. According to Dr Gudger the digestive juices of the tiger shark consist largely of strong hydrochloric acid.

Dr Gudger, however, refused to believe tales of living men being attacked and eaten by sharks, although one harpooned shark came up to the bow of his boat, gripped the stem in its jaws and tore away some of the wood. He was at a loss to explain the stomach contents of sharks. He said: "A shark ought to die of indigestion, but yet no dead tiger shark has been found with an overloaded stomach." He accepted the explanation of Stewart

Springer that sharks can relax their stomach muscles and by squeezing the body cavities eject its contents.

When considering the shark's digestion or its reactions and behaviour, one must be careful not to be "anthropomorphic" — that is, to imagine sharks think, act, eat or have teeth, insides or other parts like those of human beings. In fact, sharks' intestinal canals, when judged by human standards, are most peculiar, and there is little analogy between their processes of digestion and those of men and mammals. Whereas the intestinal canal of a 180 centimetre man is nearly 9 metres long, the length in a 3 metre shark would not exceed 2.7 metres.

Popular belief also credits sharks with insatiable voracity, but this is not true of sharks in captivity. Information supplied by the Taronga Park Zoo, Sydney, indicates that the amount of food required to sustain captive sharks is small and even large sharks appear to be light feeders. It was also found that a shark's appetite varies with the seasons.

Taronga Park Zoo some years ago had two famous captive sharks — Skipper IV and Skipper V. Skipper IV measured 3.1 to 3.3 metres and weighed approximately 153 kilograms. Skipper V was about 2.7 metres long. In the twelve months ending January 1939, Skipper IV ate approximately 81 kilograms of fish and Skipper V ate 91 kilograms. This is an average of from a quarter to one and a half kilograms of fish a day. During the whole of the winter months, May to August, Skipper IV ate only 9.5 kilograms and Skipper V only 7 kilograms.

Another strange thing about the digestion of sharks is that their stomachs can apparently not only digest food, but also hold and preserve it undigested for long periods.

A former chairman of the Taronga Park Trust, Sir Edward Hallstrom, supplied some interesting facts concerning a tiger shark which, on 23 August 1950, was placed in a large pool at Taronga Park Zoo, Sydney. It was uninjured and in good condition. As a result of this publicity given this shark Sir Edward received an inquiry: "Do sharks have the ability to store food in reserve until it is required for use?" He said he did not know, but added:

After a few days the shark regurgitated some pine leaves similar to those growing along Manly Beach, some tins and

*other litter. After this it commenced to eat the horseflesh
offered to it. I know now this was an error—it should have
been given fish.*

*The meat, apparently, was not acceptable to the shark's
stomach and was regurgitated several days later. We tried
again with horseflesh with the same result. After the shark had
been in captivity for some twenty-one days, it was noticed its
colour was becoming paler, which is a sure sign the shark will
not remain with you much longer. The shark died on 23rd
September 1950.*

*On being removed from the pool, the shark was opened.
There was found in its stomach—whether it was a reserve
compartment or a portion closed off I am unable to say—two
dolphins about four feet [1.2 metres] long in a perfect state of
preservation. These two dolphins were probably freshly taken
by the shark before its capture but how they remained in the
stomach uninjured and whilst other food was being
regurgitated is a problem to which I am unable to give the
answer.*

Sir Edward finished his report: "Conclusion: shark died of
'dolphinitis'."

Whilst fish are the staple diet of sharks, many sharks appear
to show no discrimination whatever in their feeding habits. The
long and odd list of what has been found in their stomachs
includes almost everything edible and inedible that occurs in
the upper levels of the ocean.

In their fish diet, they appear to be equally lacking in
discrimination, for it includes species as well protected as the
armoured trunk-fish, the pincushion, the porcupine fish and
stingrays, which sometimes leave their sharp bony stings
embedded inside the shark's mouth.

Sharks eat other sharks, even smaller members of their own
tribe. Some sharks specialise in shellfish. Most of them relish
squid and octopus. Turtles they consume shell and all. They
vary the menu with seabirds, sea lions and young porpoises,
swallowed whole.

Human remains are also found quite frequently inside sharks.
At one time it was widely believed that sharks would not attack
dead bodies. If a mutilated body was washed up on the shore

or human remains were found inside a shark it was assumed the person was attacked while alive. There is ample evidence, however, to prove that sharks commonly mutilate dead bodies.

More than one shark at times takes part in the mutilation of a dead body, and it is possible that for some weeks afterwards portions of human remains will be found in numerous sharks in the vicinity.

In September 1935 a waterside worker, Patrick Quinn, was lost overboard one night when he was working on a sugar lighter at Flat Top, near Mackay, Queensland. Lifebuoys were immediately thrown to Quinn and he grabbed one. A boat was lowered. It had almost reached Quinn when he was suddenly plucked from the lifebuoy and disappeared.

Three weeks later, on 31 October, crew members of the sugar cargo ship *Aldinga* caught a 3.5 metre shark. Inside it were several human bones, including the bones of a lower leg and foot with a boot on. Shortly after this a shark was caught at Flat Top by the crew of the cargo ship *Alynbank*. This one also contained human bones. In both instances the remains are believed to be those of the unfortunate Quinn.

The remarkable feature of this incident is that not only were the man's remains found in two sharks, but they were recovered in the sharks' stomachs weeks after his disappearance. Similar findings are common. Human remains appear capable of remaining for days and even weeks undigested in a shark's stomach. It was this that made the Sydney "Shark Arm" case possible. In a later chapter there is a description of an attack on a young woman who had her left arm taken off by a shark at Broome, Western Australia. The shark was caught five days later and the arm recovered from the stomach. It showed few signs of digestion. There are numerous other instances.

On 5 January 1949, three amateur fishermen, Frank and John Sorrell and Ken Marshall, set hand lines about 6 kilometres off Leighton, Western Australia. Some hours later they hauled in seven sharks, including a 2.5 metre tiger still alive. They took their catch up the Swan River to Rocky Bay and began cleaning it. When the stomach of the tiger shark was opened, a small human hand, partly decomposed, was found inside. There were other bones too, probably those of a rabbit or wallaby.

For some time police thought the hand might have belonged

TOP: *Human remains found in a shark caught on 15 January 1959, believed to be hand and other parts of 17-year-old Allan Quartly, who disappeared 15 days before from the liner* Stratheden.

BOTTOM: *A 3.5 metre shark which was caught near bathers at Chinaman's Beach and towed a boat round Sydney Harbour before it was captured.*

to 54-year-old Albert Pennington, who had been missing from Lemnos Hospital since 22 December, or to the 17-year-old bellboy Alan Quartly, who was missing from the liner *Stratheden* when it sailed from Fremantle on 21 December. Subsequently these two men were accounted for. It was then found that the hand belonged to young Arthur Strahan, aged 17, of Moora, who had disappeared while swimming at Lancelin Island on 27 December.

The Chief Inspector of Fisheries, Mr A. J. Fraser, remarked at the time it seemed almost incredible to him that a human hand in a shark's stomach would not have been completely digested within ten days. Yet there is considerable evidence to suggest this is the rule and not the exception.

In another Western Australian instance a fisherman, Allan Warne, caught a 1.4 metre tiger on one of his lines at Safety Bay on 9 March 1950. He landed it in his boat and cleaned it. Checking the contents of the stomach he found the partly decomposed right hand of a man.

Police found the hand was from the body of Peter Szot, a young Polish migrant of Perth, whose body had been washed up at City Beach on 1 March, eight days previously. The right hand was missing and there was a bullet wound in the head. He had suicided.

In the case of Mary Passaris, of Broome, the arm had remained undigested in the shark's stomach for five days. In the famous "Shark Arm" mystery described next, the arm must have been in the shark a maximum of eighteen or a minimum of eight days. In the *Aldinga* tragedy the remains — the state of digestion of them was not reported — were discovered and identified after three weeks.

Undoubtedly the most famous illustration of the length of time human remains can remain undigested in a shark's stomach was the fantastic series of events which led to what has become known in world medico-legal history as the "Aquarium Mystery" or the "Shark Arm Murder". Sir Victor Coppleson was closely associated with this case as an expert witness. Here is the story.

On 17 April 1935, Albert Edward Hobson left a bait for sharks about 2 kilometres off Coogee Beach, near Sydney. Next morning he found he had hooked a small shark but there was only a portion of it left. Most of it had been eaten by a large tiger shark about 4 metres long which was tangled up in the line. Hobson secured this shark and towed it to the beach, where he and his brother decided to place it in the Coogee Aquarium for public exhibition.

From 18 April people crowded into the aquarium to see the monster. Fresh seawater was pumped into the pool daily and the captive was fed on mackerel. For several days it ate everything thrown to it. It then went on a starvation diet and on 24 April it seemed irritable and out of sorts.

Next day some strange things happened. The events were witnessed by a small crowd of 14 people, amongst whom was Narcisse Leo Young, a proofreader on the *Sydney Morning Herald*. At the police court Young later described what took place.

The slow-moving shark, he said, suddenly increased its pace. It bumped hard against the side of the pool and then swam towards the shallow end where it appeared to turn in a sort of irregular circle two or three times. Young was about 3 or 4 metres from the shark. He noticed near it what looked like brown scum with a frightful smell. He then saw the shark regurgitate a human arm.

Albert Hobson corroborated this. He said he noticed the shark appeared very irritable and sick about 4.30 p.m. The water around it suddenly became discoloured. When it cleared, he saw floating in the water a bird, a rat, a lot of slime and a portion of a human arm with a piece of rope attached to it.

The police took the arm to the city morgue. Next day Coppleson was asked by the Government Medical Officer, Dr Arthur Palmer, to call at the morgue and examine it with him.

Together they studied it. It was a whole arm—forearm and hand—of a very muscular man with a slightly faded coloured tattoo of two boxers shaping up to each other on the forearm. It had a piece of rope about 1.4 metres long tied in two half hitches around the wrist. In front of the arm above the elbow was a large, straight gash.

It was Coppleson's opinion that the arm had not been bitten from the body by a shark because it had been cleanly disarticulated at the shoulder joint. There were no jagged edges to the flesh wound or marks of shark's teeth on the exposed cartilage of the joint. The arm had obviously been removed with

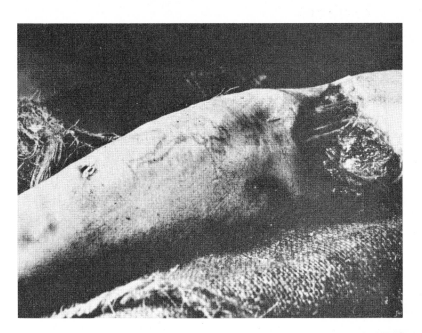

TOP: *The Shark Arm case. The arm of James Smith.*
BOTTOM: *The Shark Arm case. The shark in Coogee Aquarium, April 1935.*

a knife. It had not been removed surgically, as there was no allowance for the usual skin flaps a surgeon would use. This also ruled out a theory that the most probable source of the arm was from the body of a soldier who had some days previously committed suicide by throwing himself into the sea over a sheer rock precipice known as The Gap.

It was decided inquiries should be made to see if an arm had been removed for anatomical dissection from the Anatomy School or from a post-mortem department.

For the first time the fantastic theory of murder was raised. A Sydney newspaper, *Truth*, published a description and photograph of the tattoo. This brought quick results, for soon afterwards, a man reported he believed the arm was that of his brother, 45-year-old James Smith, a billiard marker and ex-amateur boxer. Later he positively identified it.

It the meantime the shark became very sick and on 27 April it was killed. When it was opened there were found in its stomach a portion of another shark and some fish bones, but no more human remains.

Then began a series of murder trials with few parallels in the history of crime.

Presenting a difficult case, the Crown alleged that a number of men, including Smith, Patrick Brady, a boat-builder named Reginald Holmes and several others, were involved in standover tactics, murder threats, forgery and a conspiracy to defraud an insurance company of a large sum of money by deliberately wrecking a yacht called the *Pathfinder*. The scheme misfired and it is believed that the disputes which as a result began amongst the conspirators led to a chain of events which ended in Smith's death.

The story moved to Cronulla, then a seaside resort near Sydney. Here, in March 1935, Brady, under an assumed name, had leased a cottage known as Cored Joy.

Smith was last seen alive at 6 p.m. on 8 April, playing dominoes in a hotel at Cronulla with Brady and two local residents. Nothing more was heard of him until his right arm was found in the Coogee Aquarium on 25 April.

Early on 9 April Brady had paid the rent of the cottage and then taken a taxi to Sydney, where he had seen Holmes. Next day he had visited two second-hand shops. At one he had bought a mattress, at the other a tin trunk, and had taken both purchases to Cored Joy.

From these facts the police deduced the theory that Smith had been murdered on the night of 8 April and that his body had been dismembered on a mattress and the parts stuffed into a tin trunk. The trunk had then been taken in the boat, weighed down with a kellick and other heavy objects and sunk in deep water. The police believed all the body could not be fitted into the trunk and that in the case of the arm, a rope had been tied around the wrist and it had been thrown overboard attached to a heavy weight.

On this theory the shark must have taken the arm at some time between 8 April, when Smith was last seen alive, and 17 April, when the shark was caught at Coogee. The arm must have remained in the stomach of the shark for a further eight days until it was disgorged on 25 April.

The police made a thorough search of the waters of Port Hacking for the trunk. They scoured the area with an aeroplane and a launch. A diver was sent down but he failed to locate either the trunk or any parts of a body.

On 16 May, Patrick Brady was arrested and charged with Smith's murder. Next day Holmes was questioned by the police, and he promised to give evidence at the coroner's inquiry.

Three days later Holmes's speedboat was seen racing madly around Sydney Harbour. Holmes was slumped in the cockpit. A police launch and another boat with a number of men, including Holmes's brother, on board, gave chase. The speedboat was finally overtaken. Holmes was taken off and admitted to hospital, where a soft-nosed revolver bullet was extracted from a wound in his forehead.

Seven days after this incident, Holmes made an alleged statement to the police. However, his evidence was never given. The night before the inquest, Holmes was found dead in the driving seat of his car near the Sydney Harbour Bridge with a bullet through his head.

Two men, one of them a leading Sydney boat-owner, were tried for the murder of Reginald Holmes. Although it went to three trials and created legal history, the Crown case against the men failed. So ended unresolved one of the strangest cases in the annals of crime.

John Patrick Brady died in August 1965. Crime reporter Vince Kelly, who wrote the full story of Brady, his associates and the two tiger sharks in *The Shark Arm Case* (Angus & Robertson), wrote in his foreword to the revised edition that "Australian police believed he [Brady] took to the grave the vital secrets in what expert criminologists accept as the world's most bizarre unsolved crime, known internationally as the Shark Arm Case".

The mind boggles at the odds of a tiger shark swallowing a severed arm and then, while eating a smaller hooked tiger shark, becoming tangled in a fishing line and being taken alive to an aquarium, where after eight days it discharged its stomach contents: the arm, pieces of the hooked tiger shark and a partially digested mutton bird. Many stories have been written about sharks, but as happens so often in nature, fact tops even the most bizarre and skilfully scripted fiction.

SHARKS IN ACTION

Almost everyone who has seen a shark or even merely heard of sharks has a pet theory about them. Some will say dogmatically that the monsters have poor eyesight, others that they can't hear, or that they must turn on their backs to bite.

It is not hard to get into a controversy, either, concerning the speed at which the larger sharks can swim. Opinions will vary from about 10 knots to speeds that would rival many modern hydroplanes.

It is now thought that sharks cruise from speeds as slow as 0.5 kilometres per hour to 4 to 6 kilometres per hour in *Carcharhinus* (whalers), and as much as 13 to 18 kilometres per hour in makos and white sharks. The mako is the fastest-swimming shark and is reported to be capable of 50 kilometres per hour.

Hans Hass spoke about the speed of sharks. He said: "We judged their speed at between 40 and 70 knots, and later discovered that our guess may well have been correct. Many modern warships move at more than 40 knots and sharks have been seen to overtake them with ease."

Hass said he managed to get a few photographs of sharks under full steam. The blurring of the film allowed him to calculate the approximate speed of the creatures from the known shutter speed of the camera and the length of the shark.

Sharks swim sinuously and gracefully using the shape and power of their bodies. Their fins are used for steering and turning. For speed the shape of some sharks is perfectly stream-lined and white sharks and makos (blue pointers) lose nothing in efficiency in comparison even with broadbill swordfish or tuna. Mako sharks are reputed to leap over 6 metres, clearing the water like an arrow.

Unlike most other fishes, sharks do not have an air bladder to help keep them at the depth in which they want to move; therefore they must keep swimming to hold position.

Although timing a fish or shark in the water is not easy, the subject has been approached scientifically. All sorts of devices for timing have been used: stopwatches, fishometers attached to a rod to register the speed of a running line, filming devices, timing against ships and current. Using such methods, a French scientist, Professor Magnan, found the blue shark is fast, with a cruising speed of 39 kilometres per hour. Emergency speed or short bursts may be higher.

The fastest of all fish is the sailfish, which has registered up to 113 kilometres per hour. It has been estimated that the speed required by a swordfish which once drove its rapier through some 50 centimetres of hardwood sheathed with copper must have been at least 97 kilometres per hour. The maximum speed recorded for a mako shark is 56 kilometres per hour. The slowest fish is the bream, which cruises at about 2 kilometres per hour. This is slower than an octopus, which can dart about at 6.5 kilometres per hour. Compared with most of these creatures, humans as swimmers are sluggards.

Until the advent of tagging there were very few authenticated records of the speeds of sharks and fishes over long periods and distances. There was one report, however, with sufficient evidence to convince most sceptics. In June 1855, the *Rose of Sharon*, a wooden vessel of 887 tonnes, was anchored in Torres Strait on its way from Sydney to Calcutta, when some of the crew caught a 5 metre shark and brought it aboard. The lascars in the crew cut it up for food and threw overboard the head and other parts. The ship sailed that morning and anchored again at 6 p.m., having made about 130 kilometres.

At 9 p.m. the crew hooked another shark. When it was opened the stomach contained the head and other parts of the first shark. There were also tins, pieces of fowls and other refuse thrown overboard during the day.

Although tailored for speed and streamlined like an aeroplane, sharks do not spend their time swimming from one ocean to another breaking records. In general they move at an easy pace and are often immobile, using sudden bursts of speed to capture prey or for attack or escape.

Tag and release records and recaptures from commercial and recreational fishermen have greatly increased our knowledge of the movements of many types of sharks. Some sharks are migratory and the information from tags shows the direction and time of their wanderings, indicating that some species cross oceans while others move with the currents along the coasts. On the other hand, whaling ships and whaling stations have been found to be associated with resident packs of dangerous sharks while the whales were being processed. Tag and release also gives information on the growth rates, a topic on which much had previously been conjectured, but very little proved.

White sharks and tigers have been found to follow ships for long distances. US tagging scientist Jack Casey reported that a blue shark swam 5980 kilometres, while two carcharhinid sharks were recovered nearly twenty years later some 1600 kilometres from where they were released. In Australian waters, Dr Julian Pepperel, head of the NSW Fisheries Division tagging program, reported a trans-Tasman Sea crossing by a mako shark from Australia to New Zealand (a distance of 2050 kilometres) and found that the fastest rate of travel by a tagged shark was an average of 3.3 kilometres a day for a whaler shark in its 86 days of freedom. This contrasts with some of Jack Casey's Atlantic taggings and recoveries, where 2413 kilometres in three months or 28 kilometres a day has been recorded for an Atlantic mako.

Notwithstanding the long distances travelled by all the dangerous species of sharks, they are also territorial, and defence of the territory against what is seen as a large intruder may be an important reason for shark attacks. It is believed that home territories are maintained and defended by some individuals, even in species where other individuals are gregarious and travel in schools of various sizes and sexes.

The secrets of the longevity of the various shark species are also gradually being uncovered by tagging studies. A school shark measuring 127 centimetres and estimated at nine and a half years old when tagged in 1951 measured 154 centimetres when re-caught nine years later, a growth of about 3 centimetres per year. It has been reported that male white sharks do not reach sexual maturity until they are about 3.3 metres long. The growth rate of the various species varies dramatically, from more than 300 millimetres per year to as little as 33 millimetres per year, a factor that varies with species, age and maturity.

Female sharks are generally wider, heavier and bigger than the males of the same species, probably because of the young that many species have to be able to carry within their body cavity. The large species of sharks produce their young alive and have evolved elaborate methods of nourishing them. (Other smaller types lay eggs covered with a thick, horny skin, while yet others are oviparous and keep the eggs within the female's stomach and then give birth to live sharks. The number and size of the unborn baby sharks varies from species to species. White sharks and grey nurses for example are reported to produce only one or two young at a time, whereas tigers may carry as many as fifty fully formed young.

Sharks are not alone on their travels. Some other fishes, far from avoiding them, actively seek out their company. Pilot fish, which are attractive little creatures, slender with black and silver or steel blue stripes, and shorter and chubbier fish known as sergeant-majors, often accompany oceanic sharks. Groups of five or more of these pilots can often be seen swimming along in perfect V-formation in the bow wave of the shark.

It is difficult to understand what mutual service is performed by these little fishes and their big companions. Many say the pilot fish guide the sharks to their prey and live on the tiny morsels which escape their great jaws. But scientists today tend to disregard this "blind man's guide dog" theory, as it is now known that sharks not only see very well, but can also use other senses to find prey very efficiently, as will be seen later.

Other strange companions of the cruising sharks are the remoras or sucking fish, which are "hangers on" and "hitchhikers" — literally. They are gracefully shaped, with long slender bodies. At the top of the remora's head is a flat, elongated disc with transverse ridges like a venetian blind. This is the sucker, and with it the remora can cling to a smooth object — or a shark — with incredible tenacity. The open ocean shark has the pilots hanging round for a free meal and the remoras for a free ride.

But these nuisances are not the worst of the monster's troubles. If a shark could talk it would no doubt spend most of its time complaining about the sea lice and other parasites. The latter are often difficult to detect, as they are flush with the skin near the vent and assume the skin's colour. It is often said that sharks cruise into brackish water to rid themselves of the parasites, which drop off in fresh water. Normally ocean-swimming sharks have been recorded in underwater caves in Mexico which have water of lower salinity because of fresh water intake through the sand. It is conjectured that these large sharks have gone there to rest and to rid themselves of parasites.

Experienced divers believe that sharks can communicate with one another. It raises the question of shark talk, of what they hear and say to one another. It has long been known that fish utter an astonishingly wide variety of strange sounds like distant bells, clickings, grunts, moans, groans, coos and growls. For centuries, the Japanese have trained underwater listeners to locate shoals of fish. They can detect not only the direction of the shoals but the particular kinds of fish. But whether the sounds indicate warnings, fighting, courtship or merely idle gossip, no one has been able to say. It is reported that a shark which attacked a girl at Margate in Natal, South Africa, grunted loudly as it attacked and that a female tiger shark caught in a trawling net in New Zealand threshed wildly about the deck and barked like a dog.

An obvious first step in a study of the reactions of sharks is at least to obtain a rudimentary idea of their sense organs and of what a shark's world is like. In order to make such a study and learn something of the behaviour patterns and responses of sharks, special pens for large sharks were built in the shallow waters of Binimi in the Bahamas by Michael Lerner.

These ingenious shark pens included a special operating section, into which the shark can be guided, there to be secured in a net and lifted out of the water by an overhead crane.

Dr Perry Gilbert designed these facilities to enable him to administer an anaesthetic to a shark, then temporarily to blind it or block its sense of smell. Dr Gilbert is now Director of the Mote Marine Laboratory, Cape Haze, Florida.

In another pen, the reactions of sharks either operated on or normal can be observed and recorded by a special motion picture camera. Tests are being made with chemicals, foods and physiological fluids such as blood to determine which attract and which repel sharks under various conditions and to test the repellent action of various substances such as octopus ink, sea cucumber toxins and similar substances.

While we can hardly apply to sharks and fish, immersed in a fluid medium, the notions of hearing or smell as we conceive them on land, there can be little doubt that they have highly developed comparable senses.

Those who have studied the anatomy of sharks' brains have been particularly impressed by the high degree of development of those parts of their brains associated with the sense of smell. This, together with the intricate system of folds (Schneider folds) in their nostrils, leaves little doubt about the important part the sense of smell must play in their daily lives. The attraction of offal to sharks is well known. Reported experiments suggest they can detect offal and other odoriferous substances at considerable distances. Even the smell of fish or bait in a boat can attract them. It suggests that a bather handling fish before a swim is taking a risk should there be a hungry shark in the vicinity. For ears, sharks have two tiny channels or pits in their heads lined with sensitive hairs.

Little is known about the shark's sense of touch. They often investigate strange objects by butting against them or nudging them and it is possible that they rely for touch mainly on the tips of their snouts and the leading edges of their fins.

The next chapter discusses instances of sharks butting against surf skis, surfboards and other floating objects. It also suggests the approach of sharks to swimmers, especially in the open sea, is often of this nature and the sharks' objective is investigation rather than attack.

In addition, to enable them to adapt themselves to their watery world, sharks and fish possess a collection of organs of special sense, which have no counterpart in humans or land animals. With these senses they perceive sensations and gain information about their surroundings beyond our comprehension and even difficult for us to imagine. The best known of these sense organs are the sensorial canals, the ampullae or flasks of Lorenzini and the sensorial crypts. Sharks are particularly provided with them. As navigational and other aids, they are essential to the sharks' existence. For their description, the authors are indebted to Professor Paul Budker's book, *La Vie des Requins*.

The *sensorial canals* are the shark's radar — its apparatus for picking up vibrations in water. For many years their function was not understood but the principle on which they work is very simple.

The canals are embedded in the deeper layers of the shark's

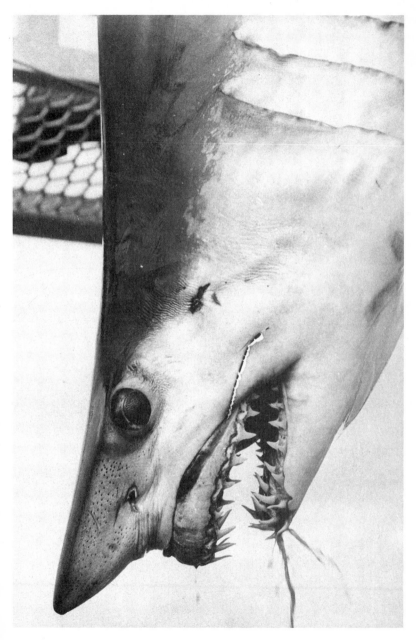

A mako shark with its teeth exposed. The pores of the ampullae of Lorenzini and other receptors in the nose can be clearly seen. PETER GOADBY

skin. They communicate with the surface by means of numerous tubules, which open on the skin at regular intervals. Both the tubules and canals are filled with mucus.

Vibrations reaching the openings of the tubules act upon the mucus. This transmits impulses right along the back into the canals, where they are registered by special cells in the canal walls. These cells then communicate the impulses to the shark's brain and thus keep the shark informed of its surroundings.

In addition to sensing the vibrations, it is probable that from their stength and character the shark is able to judge their origin, distance and source.

Some of the canals occupy a position along the shark's sides corresponding to the lateral lines of the bony fishes. Others are situated on the shark's head, circling its eye sockets and following the line of its jaws. The bony fishes have a system similar in principle, but the openings of the tubules are related to definite and easily recognisable lateral lines; in sharks they are hidden by skin denticles.

Experiments have shown that sharks can locate their prey in open sea and dirty water or even buried on the sea bottom by receiving minute electric forces. The reception devices on the sharks are called the *ampullae of Lorenzini*.

These organs enable them to detect very small electric fields associated with animals or with metal. Kalmijn, who established the function of the ampullae of Lorenzini, also believes that sharks may use these in navigation, as they would be sensitive to the earth's magnetic field. He reported that the sharks responded to "voltage gradients as low as one hundred millionth of a volt per centimetre". This remarkable sensitivity to voltage is far greater than that known to be possessed by any other animal. It is believed also that the ampullae are used by the shark at close range as a substitute for vision when feeding or attacking. At such times the shark may be unable to see because the eye has been covered by the nictitating membrane or has been rolled back as the jaws have opened.

The *sensorial crypts* provide sharks with a water sampling apparatus that enables them to detect changes in the chemistry and salinity of the water. The crypts are associated with skin denticles. They present the following features.

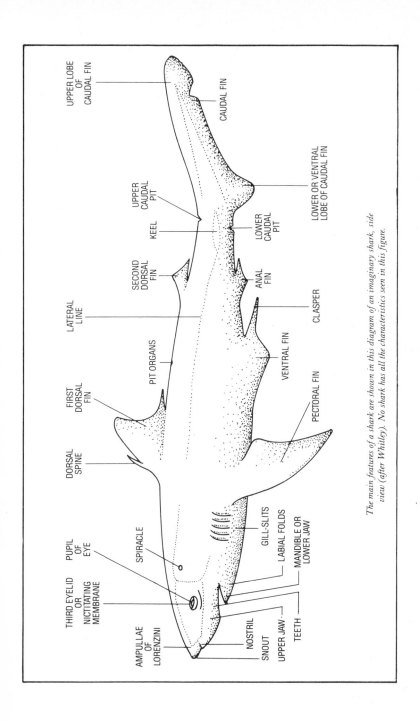

The main features of a shark are shown in this diagram of an imaginary shark, side view (after Whitley). No shark has all the characteristics seen in this figure.

Two adjacent scales or denticles, differentiated from the rest, overlap each other in such a way as to leave between them a small crypt or cavity. In young sharks these differentiated scales form a clearly visible ridge, but in older sharks they merge into the rest of the scales. The crypts are most numerous in ocean-going or pelagic sharks.

Inside the crypt is a papilla and a large sensitive cell. The remarkable thing about this arrangement is that it is indistinguishable from the papillae and cells which constitute the taste buds in human and animal tongues.

Whilst the deduction of function from structure is generally frowned upon in scientific circles, the resemblance of these cells and papillae to the taste buds of humans and animals is so striking that it surely gives a lead to their probable function. Perhaps, as maintained by some, the back and sides of an animal is a strange distribution for organs of taste, but effective experiments confirm that these structures are sensitive to chemical stimuli. This supports the view that they are destined for the perception of taste. It also distinguishes them from the two other sensory organs mentioned, both of which react to mechanical stimuli.

Sea legends and popular belief once held that most shark species have poor eyesight. Research by Dr Perry Gilbert of Florida's Mote laboratory has shown that the shark's eyes are in fact well adapted for seeing in dark and cloudy water. Laboratory tests have proved that sharks do in fact use their eyes in seeking and taking food. Before they move into their feeding pattern, large dangerous sharks of many species can detect and will shy away from movement such as upraised arms. However, once in their feeding pattern, sharks will ignore movement above and below the surface and will continue to attack and feed even if beaten around the head.

Scientific tests by Dr Gilbert and others, and observations by fishermen, have shown that sharks have more than adequate eyesight in a wide range of light conditions. Sharks are conscious of violent or aggressive moves towards them either above or below the surface. Below the surface all species, before adopting the attack or feeding pattern, appear conscious of being watched by human eyes, and white sharks and to a lesser extent tigers exhibit awareness of being watched from above the surface also.

Sharks can also undoubtedly see some distance outside the water. Some say for 2.5 to 3 metres, and cite the sharks at Darwin in northern Australia, which regularly leap high into the air to snatch flying-foxes from overhanging branches.

Sharks' eyes are large in proportion to the size of their bodies and much flatter than human eyes. Contrary to popular belief, their eyes are shaped for distant sight, but are capable of a considerable range of near vision. To focus their eyes sharks move the whole lens system backwards and forwards like a miniature magnifying glass.

Light rapidly fades as it descends below the surface. This limits the underwater vision of a human in a mask under the best conditions to a distance of about 20 metres. But nature has provided the shark with a special mechanism at the back of its eye to make the most of dim illumination. This apparently not only enables sharks to penetrate the gloom of the depths during the day, but also to see well in the dark. A similar mechanism is found at the back of the eyes of most nocturnal animals. This is the layer which reflects light and makes cats' eyes appear to shine at night. The shark, however, unlike the cat, can turn it on and off, as required.

Another change associated with the natural adaptation of animals' eyes to dim light is an increase in the light-perceiving cells or rods at the expense of the cones or colour-perceiving cells. It supports the views of those who claim sharks are colour-blind. (But see below.)

Besides these adaptations of its eye to the environment, the shark has a third eyelid (nictitating membrane) like many of the birds. Its function is probably, as in the birds, to clean the surface of the eye or protect its more delicate layers from bright sunlight.

Many practical experts, however, disagree that sharks are colour-blind. On the theory that they are colour sensitive there were official proposals during World War II that rafts should be painted certain colours to protect them. Blue in particular was suggested. Experiments have demonstrated attack reactions by dangerous sharks to the bright yellow and orange used in safety garments. Nevertheless, bright yellow and orange increase safety in other ways by being more visible to searchers in all light conditions.

Dr Bombard, who some years ago sailed the Atlantic alone on his raft, the *Heretique*, without food or water to prove he could maintain himself purely from the sea, said he found yellow attracted sharks and other large sea creatures and that he was unable to keep some vivid yellow rubberised cloth attached to the floats of the raft to protect him from breaking waves, because they jumped out of the water and tore it off.

There is also widespread belief that sharks are attracted more by white than dark objects. For instance, it is said they prefer pale fish to dark ones; that they will attack people with white skins in preference to dark and are attracted by the lighter coloured palms of the hands and soles of the feet of dark-skinned people.

It is claimed that throwing white sheets of paper on the water will act as a decoy. In experiments carried out with white and dark bait some observers said the sharks fought for the white and disregarded the dark. On these grounds it has been suggested bathers should wear dark costumes for protection against attack.

Statistics lend little support to the theory. The truth appears to be that the shark does not discriminate. It attacks what is available — dark and coloured swimmers mainly in the tropics and white swimmers in the rest of the world. Among instances cited in this book, there are only two reports of bathers being attacked while wearing white.

Like most underwater creatures, sharks are inquisitive. Unfamiliar objects arouse their curiosity. They will often remain motionless for long periods, watching and gazing at anything strange, especially if it is stationary. At times they will swim around or approach it in a series of diminishing circles. They may nose or nudge it or rush and strike it with their body or fins. Some of the scavengers, like the whalers, however, often seize objects immediately they are thrown in the water.

On one of his expeditions, Jacques Cousteau watched oceanic white tips, blue sharks and other carcharinids from a shark cage. He later remarked on the gradually diminishing circles the sharks swam as they approached any object that aroused their curiosity. He summed up: "The sharks took a long time surveying submerged men and seemed to sense danger in all divers."

Similar cages are now currently used for study and photography of sharks of many species, including the great white shark, in their home environment. Much has been learned, yet there still remains a tremendous amount to be discovered before we can prove what attracts and what repels sharks, what triggers the various kinds of attacks and what will give protection. The manner in which sharks act before attack, and visibly show annoyance and give warning, is now being recorded for some dangerous species. Filming by divers and surface observation by fishermen have also increased our knowledge.

Some species in coral reef areas, particularly the grey reef shark (*Carcharhinus amblyrhynchos*), show what appear to be warning poses, indicating aggression towards other animals in their territory. In most species, when excited, there is a change in swim pattern from the apparently leisurely sinuous cruising mode to a stiffer, tail-banging, head-swinging, excited movement through the water.

Species such as tiger sharks, blue sharks and the various *Carcharhinus* species (whalers) have nictitating membranes and will, when approaching and excited, often slide that membrane over the eye. Other species which lack nictitating membranes, such as makos and white sharks with their large dark eyes, roll the eye back so that the white part of the eyeball shows instead of the dark of the pupil. This visible warning can be beneficial to divers and others who may be in proximity to these species. The sliding of the nictitating membrane or rolling back of the eye is an indication of excitement and the possibility of a feeding frenzy.

There is no doubt that while sharks will occasionally attack humans, the trigger that causes the attack is not positively defined. Blood in the water, panic vibration, the sudden isolation of one person, hunger, and the need to enforce territorial rights, are all reliably and logically believed to be triggers. Al Giddings of Ocean Images in California has shown photographically the resemblance of a human on a short surfboard to a seal in the water when silhouetted against the light, suggesting that mistaken identity may be a reason for some attacks. Low frequency sounds in the 20 to 40 hertz range have been demonstrated in French Polynesia to attract grey reef sharks and incite them to a feeding frenzy.

Shark species other than the lamnids (the whites, makos and porbeagles) are cold-blooded. The lamnids to varying extents

A tiger shark showing the nictitating membrane moving to cover the eye.
RON AND VALERIE TAYLOR

have blood which is several degrees warmer than the water in which they cruise. The members of this family whose home environment is the colder waters show this characteristic to a greater extent than the warm water member of their family, the long fin mako.

Temperature levels and changes in temperature greatly influence movements, activities and attack behaviour. It seems possible to be much more explicit than these vague generalisations. When attacks in various parts of the world are examined, it will be seen that most attacks take place in water warmer than 20°C. This is also the temperature condition when most humans are enjoying themselves in the sea. The dangerous *Carcharhinus* (whaler) sharks and the tiger shark are expected in the tropical and subtropical waters, whereas the white shark, a cool water species, usually contributes the danger in water temperatures below 20°C.

All fishermen know and recognise the influence of water temperature on the prevalence and availability of fish species. The warm water of the ocean current carries not only the great pelagic species of marlin and tuna but naturally also the sharks that prey on these species. In Australia midsummer, the time of maximum water temperature inshore as well as offshore, is the time when the whalers and the ocean-going tiger sharks move in close to shore in numbers, and some — perhaps to spawn, perhaps to rid themselves of parasites — move into waters of lower salinity in the bays, estuaries and rivers where they are then in close proximity to the maximum number of people in those same waters, there to relax, to enjoy the waters and to cool off from the high daily temperature.

Dr David Davies of the South African Association for Marine Biological Research, in his book *About Sharks and Shark Attack*, covering the sharks and attacks in South African waters, also draws attention to the increase in shark attacks and shark activity in waters above 20°C.

Dr David Baldridge, who analysed shark attacks for the US Shark Research Panel and supervised the Shark Attack File, in his book and papers expressed the opinion that the reason why attacks were so much more frequent in waters above 20°C was that this temperature was the threshold of comfort for humans, so that there were more people in water above 20°C and thus more chance of attack. Both opinions have some truth. However, the fact remains that in waters above 20°C fishermen expect a greater incidence of sharks and a greater variety of species, including some of the most potentially dangerous and numerous species: the whalers, of which 14 of the 25 acknowledged species are considered dangerous, and another known man-eater, the tiger shark.

Thus, when the water is warm, more people are in the water, and with more whalers and tiger sharks, than at any other time. The humans are swimming, surfboarding, snorkelling, spearfishing and diving with scuba. When silhouetted against the surface in these activities, they are most liable to be attacked and are at their greatest disadvantage.

Attacks in the cooler waters, (below 20°C), the environment of the white shark in many countries and continents, have increased with the increase in surface and subsurface use of these waters made possible by the use of wetsuits.

The incidence of attacks and menacing of surface board riders and spearfishermen has increased since the wetsuit became available. Dr Baldridge's 1974 statistics showed that 90 per cent of attacks were right at the surface. Miller and Collier in 1981 showed the percentage as 79 per cent and noted that only 8 of 43 victims observed the sharks before being attacked, and only 3 of 42 victims were attacked frontally. Feet and legs were most commonly attacked, followed by arms and hands.

Most observers agree that probably the greatest attractor of sharks' attention is fish — especially hooked and struggling fish. It is a common observation amongst spearfishermen that they are able to move underwater for long periods unmolested whilst searching for fish but the moment they spear a fish, a shark appears apparently from nowhere.

William Beebe, in the account of his *Zaca* expedition, described how, having hooked a groper, he alternately hauled it in and then let it run free on the line. While doing this, he closely watched the reactions of a sea perch and two sharks that waited inquiringly by. Each time he hauled in the fish and it resisted, flapping, one of the predatory fish came shooting up. If Beebe slackened off on the line, so that the groper regained its balance and its normal appearance, the robbers stopped immediately and watched the fish "like growling dogs that mean

TOP: *A pack of whaler sharks weighing between 135 and 180 kg swoops, and all that is left of a 454 kg white shark is the tail.* DENNIS HILL

BOTTOM: *Grey reef sharks biting one another as they are about to go into a feeding frenzy.* RON AND VALERIE TAYLOR

to bite and are waiting only for another movement to snap".

It is also well known that bright objects and metal attract sharks. In at least one instance the flash of a ring on the finger has been blamed for an attack. Some of the experiences of spearfishermen suggest the attention of the shark was drawn to them by their equipment.

An example of this is provided by the experience of Rex Gallagher, a 25-year-old spearfisherman of Shellharbour, New South Wales, during February 1953.

Gallagher went spearfishing using a snorkel and wearing an underwater mask with a bright metal band. It was about 6 p.m. and he was concentrating on a dying groper. He sent a shaft deep into the groper. Then, out of spears, he surfaced, borrowed another gun and sent a second spear into it as it came out of its cave. What interested Gallagher was that it was followed out of the cave by a large brown wobbegong shark with three or four tentacles hanging from its lip. Discretion being the better part of valour, Gallagher swam away within 30 centimetres of the bottom for about 15 metres and then saw the shark rushing in to attack him.

Its objective was obviously the mask. It tore away the face piece and snapped off the snorkel. The impetus of the rush was so great that the shark and the spearfisherman were both hurled from the water. Gallagher received injuries to the face and nose and under the chin.

Another widely held view is that the smell of blood is almost irresistible to a shark. Thor Heyerdahl, the leader of the *Kon-Tiki* expedition, who had considerable time and opportunity for studying the habits and reactions of the large sharks which followed his raft, came to this conclusion, and believed it was smell rather than sight which excited a shark's voracity. He wrote:

> *We have sat with our legs in the water to test them and they have swum towards us till they were two or three feet [0.6 to 0.9 metre] away, only quietly to turn their tails towards us again. But if the water was in the least bloodstained, as it was when we had been cleaning fish, the sharks' fins came to life and they would suddenly collect like bluebottles from a long way off. If we flung out sharks' guts, they simply went mad and dashed about in a blind frenzy. They savagely devoured*

the liver of their own kind, and then if we put a foot into the
sea they came for it like rockets and even dug their teeth into
the logs where the foot had been.

But whether blood alone is such an attraction for sharks is
questionable, for on many occasions the use of large quantities
of bullock's blood to attract man-killers responsible for attacks
has failed to attract them or any other shark.

By contrast, Albert Tester found that sharks which had not
fed recently responded to fish flesh in the water in dilutions of
only one part in ten million parts of sea water.

Bruce Wright, who commanded a British sea reconnaissance
unit during World War II, made a special investigation of the
underwater reactions of sharks to blood and movement. He
concluded that blood alone, unaccompanied by movement, had
no effect on either sharks or barracuda, but that rapid jerky
movements, with or without fish blood, excited them.

It is ironic that in addition to the attraction that sharks have
for safety yellow, the vibration and air pattern created by
thumping on the water from helicopters often used in rescues
should also be an attractant to a curious predatory shark. Other
attractants to sharks are underwater explosions and low frequency electronic vibrations. Research has shown that sharks
detect vibrations through their ears, which are in the cartilage
around the brain cavity. Knowledge and recognition of attractants are an important factor in the search for repellents.

Some evidence supports the view that sharks preparing to
attack may be frightened away if the intended victim is joined
by others. Later, when attacks on bathers are considered, it will
be seen that there is also reason to believe the converse is true.
This means, if a number of bathers are close together in the
water and all leave except one—this happens when surfers catch
a wave to shoot back to the shore—the bather left is more
susceptible to attack.

One of the most interesting and perhaps important theories
on the reactions of sharks is sometimes referred to as the "scream
theory". This is that sharks can not only detect shouting underwater, but may actually be deterred from an impending attack
by this means.

France, in his *Wonders of Life in the Animal World*, states that the pearl divers of Sri Lanka, who ply their trade amid swarms of sharks, confine their efforts to chasing them off merely to shouting. Since then, numerous observers, notably Dr Hans Hass, have claimed that aggressive sharks can be scared off in this way.

"None of our observations," Hass wrote in his *Diving to Adventure*, "attracted so much interest and attention when published as the discovery that aggressive sharks could be scared off by shouting underwater." This method proved its usefulness on several occasions when he was attacked. Each time the sharks fled.

Opinions differ on whether the effect is due to vibrations received by the lateral lines. Some think it is caused by bubbles which accompany the scream.

Summing up the general opinion of world authorities, it seems that sharks are not a serious menace to swimmers or divers in most parts of the world, but must always be treated with respect and caution.

Captain Cousteau, who has come face to face with more than a hundred sharks, said:

> The better we are acquainted with sharks, the less we know them and one can never tell what a shark is going to do. Sharks never attack with resolution. During an encounter with a shark in the Cape Verde Islands at a distance of 40 feet [12 metres] there appeared from the grey haze the lead-white bulk of a 25-foot [7.6 metre] Carcharodon carcharias, *the only shark species that all specialists agree is a confirmed man-eater. Dumas, my bodyguard, closed in beside me. The brute was swimming lazily. Then the shark saw us. His reaction was the least conceivable one. In pure fright, the monster voided a cloud of excrement and departed at an incredible speed.

Those writing on the subject of shark behaviour often express the view that sharks are the underwater equivalent of dogs or man-eating tigers. Even the early Romans named some sharks "dogfish". Certainly, like dogs, some of the sharks are large, savage and vicious, but others are as timid as trout.

Franco Prosperi expressed the same thoughts in his book, *Lord of the Sharks*. He believes that in places where sharks have seen little of man, they hesitate before attacking. Also, Prosperi says, seasons and time of the day affect the likelihood of attack. He adds that the most important factor determining shark attacks is the species of shark involved. He considers swimmers are more likely to be attacked on the surface and the moments of greatest danger to a diver are just as he or she is about to enter or leave the water with only part of the body submerged.

Careful notes on the behaviour of sharks and barracuda in the presence of man were made by Bruce S. Wright (mentioned earlier). More than 10,000 man-hours were spent underwater, a fairly solid basis of experience. His studies on the coasts of California and the Bahamas showed that usually sharks do not attack man on sight. The findings were supported by further experience on the coast of Sri Lanka and the Arakan coast of Burma. Among the sharks encountered were many reputed man-killers, including the whaler, hammerhead, tiger and great white shark. Barracuda were also met.

His chief conclusion was that "a man in the water alone, or men in a group, acting quietly and smoothly, did not release the attack pattern of either shark or barracuda". Numerous instances will also be cited of persons bathing without molestation in shark-infested waters. There are cases of fishermen falling unharmed into the sea close to sharks generally regarded as dangerous.

In fact, experience in Australia is that throughout the year on most beaches the presence of sharks, many of them of man-killing varieties, in the vicinity of bathers appears to be the rule rather than the exception. It suggests that sharks can become accustomed to the presence of humans and that danger from sharks may be greater from visiting sharks that from the local varieties.

The predatory behaviour of sharks was also studied in field observations by von Irenaus Eibl-Eibesfeldt and Hans Hass. They found vibrations alerted sharks and attracted them at a distance, and that their rush at living prey is mainly directed by eyesight but that sharks are able to locate stationary prey by smell alone. Their observations showed that very few species will attack a human at first sight. Sharks not accustomed to people usually approach a swimmer or diver cautiously, circle round in an exploratory manner and attack only after long deliberation. All shark species observed could be repelled at least for a time.

A French naval officer who has studied the subject, Surgeon-Lieutenant Y. Gilbert-Desvallons, said that in the presence of prey a shark often gives the impression of idleness. It may be seen approaching the bait, pushing it with its snout, swimming off and returning. Americans call this "slow feeding", as distinct from "collective behaviour" or "frenzied feeding", seen under somewhat rare conditions. In the latter case sharks compete with others for possession of the prey and attack everything within range. D. J. Miller and R. S. Collier, in their paper "Shark Attacks in California and Oregon 1929-79", stated, "Most of the attacks upon humans were apparently slow, deliberate movements which could be described as investigatory interraction." John McCosker, in a scientific paper on white shark attack behaviour published in 1985, wrote:

> In all recorded North Pacific attacks on humans, the victim was then released, and the shark routinely retreated a short distance from the injured and immobilized prey, thereby allowing the victim to lapse into shock or bleed to death. In the case of human victims, I suggest the retreat behaviour has previously been misinterpreted to indicate something distasteful or offensive about human flesh and/or neoprene wetsuit material. It is commoly held that white sharks are "man biters" but not "man eaters"—a paradox when one considers the catholic nature of its diet, rather I interpret this bite and spit behaviour to be adaptive in that it reduces the injury to the shark caused by the teeth and nails of a struggling pinniped.

As the story unfolds, it will be seen there are many riddles of shark behaviour — the limitation of their attacks to certain areas, the avoidance of others, the variations in the risk of attack with seasons, conditions and places and in some parts of the world the observance of a timetable.

Researchers led by Dr Perry Gilbert and Dr Eugenie Clark, Mote Marine Laboratory, Cape Haze, Florida, have come up with much information gradually unlocking some of the shark's secrets. The statistical analysis of all shark attacks by Dr Baldridge, formerly of the US Navy and now at Mote Marine Laboratory has been invaluable in separating fact from feeling. This organised research at Cape Haze combined with the revealing movie footage of master film makers Peter Gimble, Ron and Valerie Taylor, Jacques Cousteau and others around the world, shows the shark and its reactions in its natural environment in a way never before possible. Sharks and their danger and power are now known around the world as they are rather than as figures of evil and myth.

BUMPING TACTICS

During the surfing season Sydney and Newcastle newspapers regularly report incidents involving surfboards, surf skis, their riders and sharks. They never warrant more than a small paragraph because this kind of incident is common. Should the rider get tossed into the water alongside the shark, he or she might score a few more lines. Surf skis and boards are often bumped and occasionally attacked. Like the surf reel and line the surf ski is an Australian device and its use for rescue as well as recreation is known to surf-lifesavers of other nations. Surboard riding is a worldwide sport and the boards with riders in wetsuits have brought more humans than ever into possible contact and conflict with the great white sharks as well as other dangerous species. Surfboards and surf skis are evidently objects of considerable curiosity to sharks, hence the "bumping" attacks. Attacks in which both the rider and the board, with its tough fibreglass armour, are chopped by the teeth and powerful bite are more serious in intent and effect than the "bump" attacks.

Once in a while the idyllic peaceful enjoyment of the board riders is ruined when sharks show real interest.

One hot day in November 1947 a large crowd at Newcastle sweltered on the beach for four hours watching a shark fight a battle with a whale 500 metres offshore. Later two boys went fishing from surf skis. As one of the boys was pulling in a fish, the shark—apparently it had had enough of the whale—snapped the fish from the line. It was obviously an aggressive creature, for not satisfied with a whale and the fish, it turned its attention to one of the skis. In the first run it nearly overturned the craft. Several times it shot past, turned and came in again. One of the boys felt his ski lift nearly a metre out of the water. He hung on grimly while the shark dived beneath the craft several times, sending up showers of spray. This one was 3 metres long and was badly in need of dry-docking, for it had barnacles on its tail.

Happenings like this are frequent off the Sydney and Newcastle beaches. Nobody worries much about them. It doesn't scare off any of the skiers. In fact, none of them has ever come to any harm, although some have had frightening experiences.

What is the shark's objective? It does not appear to be destructive for, while teeth marks are often left on the boards and skis, it is unusual for a second assault to take place. Nor do the sharks appear to be after the riders of the boards or skis, for although many of the riders have been thrown into the water by the force of the bump, no shark has ever turned on them. In fact, never once has a person been attacked in these circumstances, although many times the shark has had every opportunity.

There have been various explanations of the shark's strange behaviour. The one nearest the truth is probably that the bump is merely the shark's method of examining an unknown object in the same way as an animal on land often investigates an unfamiliar object with its nose.

One authority (Springer) suggests that the shark is testing the object for juices to ascertain whether it is edible. (Remember that sharks have organs of taste on their backs and sides.) Suggestions have also been made that it is merely play — the shark's idea of fun. This is not as fantastic as it might seem. Dolphins and porpoises are known to play and romp. Some say they not only dance together in the waves, but even play sides in organised games.

Usually there is only one shark to handle, but surf skiers have at times been faced with the problem of how to deal with as many as six. This happened at Avalon in February 1948, when two skiers about 200 metres from shore saw the school about 10 metres away.

The men's reactions were quite natural. They slapped the water fiercely with their paddles and then, without waiting to see how the sharks took it, raced for the shore. One shark, a little more inquisitive than the others, followed them in. Then it returned to its mates and the six of them cruised menacingly along the beach for almost an hour.

In many instances, the shark has bumped the ski violently and thrown the rider into the water. Some riders have had to abandon their skis and swim long distances to the shore. The sharks, too, have often resented efforts to drive them off and have retaliated vigorously.

At other times the boot has been on the other foot and the shark more frightened than the skiers. In January 1942 three members of the Manly Surf Club set out on surf skis for Freshwater Beach, where they expected to find better shoots. They were about half a kilometre off North Steyne when a 3.5 metre shark swam lazily under one of the skis and then made towards another.

The rider of this ski took no chances. He lifted his paddle and smacked the shark on the head. Justifiably annoyed, it thrashed the water but did nothing else. Under the impetus of three sets of churning paddles the skis planed away and the shark disappeared.

Most of these encounters have taken place at long distances from the shore. In January 1942 Roger Duck and Ray Leighton, two Manly Surf Club members, were more than 200 metres off Fairy Bower on a surf ski. When they saw a 3 metre shark, they tried to frighten it off by smacking the water with their paddles. All that happened was that the creature lost its temper. It shot in and made a vicious snap at Duck's blade. The shark then disappeared and the two men returned to shore. There were teeth marks on the paddle.

A similar thing happened to Ken Howell, Australian surf ski champion, in January 1936. He was even farther out — about 400 metres off North Bondi — with two other skiers, when a 3.5 metre shark began circling his ski. Howell tried to hit the shark with his paddle. It reacted immediately. It snapped at the paddle, bumped the ski heavily and nearly capsized it. Fortunately a big roller came along and the men reached the beach, leaving the rest of the ocean to the shark.

In most of the attacks on skis and boards the riders were able to reach the beach safely, but some tipped over and joined the shark in the water.

Don Dixon, a young lifesaver of Mona Vale, near Sydney, was waiting for a wave with a club-mate, Lindsay Paton, about 400 metres out from Mona Vale Beach, in January 1949 when the shark attacked. There was a swirl and a bump, and Dixon was in the water. The shark made a crunching sound as it smashed into the bottom of his ski. The lad kicked desperately

Sharks often investigate surf skis, surfboards, open sea swimmers, skin divers and floating objects by bumping into them.

Sharks usually approach in diminishing circles before attacking underwater or taking bait.

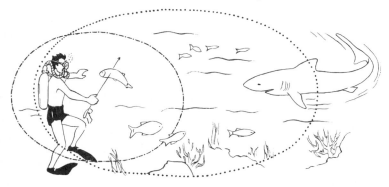

Sharks see better and further underwater than skin divers. In murky water sharks have special means of detection.

and could feel the shark swirling and threshing about underneath. Three times he fell into the water when big waves struck him but each time he managed to scramble back on the ski until finally he reached the beach. All the time the shark cruised nearby as though acting as escort.

There is the story, too, of Jack Haynes, of Maroubra Surf Club, New South Wales. In December 1953 Haynes fell off his ski into the company of a shark sadly lacking a kindly disposition. He is lucky to be alive because either the shark's aim was bad or it was intent on other things.

Haynes was about 300 metres off Maroubra Beach when he saw a shark's fin cutting the water. He paddled for the shore with such energy that he overbalanced and fell into the water. The ski drifted away and Haynes, not wishing to share the water with the 3.5 metre menace, swam furiously after the ski. Then the shark charged. The lifesaver felt a terrific surge as the big fellow shot past. Haynes climbed back on the ski and paddled furiously beachwards.

On occasions the shark's impetus overturns the ski. Ernest Baker, a member of the Cronulla Surf Club, New South Wales, found himself in this terrifying predicament one day in January 1937. One moment he was skiing pleasantly along. Then he felt a severe bump and was thrown violently into the water. Baker came to the surface and was horrified to see nothing but his overturned ski protecting him from a large shark churning the water just a metre or so away.

Sharks are noted for their speed, but that day Baker was a sight faster for he was lying flat on the keel of the ski before the shark could turn to attack. On the beach later, a thoroughly shaken Baker found deep indentations on the upper and lower sides of his ski.

Another surf skier, Gordon Hilton, of the Terrigal Surf Club, New South Wales, was hit with such force that he took to the air.

Hilton undoubtedly asked for trouble. He thought he saw a shark from the beach. He boarded his ski and paddled out about 50 metres to investigate. Looking over the side he saw the shark surfacing. It was directly under him and about 3.5 metres long. Before he had time to think he went up in the air and then back into the water. He managed to regain the surf ski and made all speed for the good dry sand.

The attacks on surfboards have followed a similar pattern.

There have been reports of sharks striking them and overturning them. Most of the surfboard attacks have also been at long distances from the shore. Since the increased popularity of the short surfboard, with riders using wetsuits, the number of attacks on board riders has increased, particularly in cooler waters.

When this strange behaviour of sharks and the reports of some of the attacks on swimmers are compared, a similarity becomes obvious. The logical conclusion is that some of the attacks on swimmers are really bumps and that wounds, often serious, are caused not by the shark's teeth and jaws but by the impact of their bodies and fins. Many victims have actually complained they felt the shark strike them.

An incident 16 kilometres from Townsville, Queensland, on 8 March 1920, first drew attention to this type of attack on swimmers. The following is the description of the incident by Dr Harold Miller of Townsville, in the *Medical Journal of Australia*, 31 July 1920.

> *A.B., aged 20, and six other men set out on 8th March 1920 in a yacht in Cleveland Bay to take stores from Townsville to the Bay Rock Lighthouse. They made a fishing trip at the same time. When about halfway between Bay Rock and Magnetic Island, the boat overturned and sank. The occupants decided to swim to Bay Rock, a distance of about three miles. A.B. had been knocked on the head with a mast and "went out to it". After coming to, he started to swim. He had been swimming for about twenty minutes, when he was attacked and bitten by a shark. The shark evidently could not get sufficient grip in the region where it set its teeth.* It then tossed A.B. out of the water a distance of several feet [about a metre]. *The shark did not trouble him again. He was then able to continue his swim and eventually reached Bay Rock. Three of the seven were lost, but the others reached the rock without being molested. Cleveland Bay is infested with sharks.*

The most puzzling feature of this case was the victim's wounds, shown in the photographs which accompanied Dr Miller's article and reproduced in this book. There are what appear to be single rows of teeth marks on the front and back of the body corresponding to the upper and lower jaws of a large shark. The wounds were not deep.

It is hard, however, to believe that a man could have been

seized in the jaws of a large shark violently enough to have been thrown into the air and escape with such superficial and "dainty" wounds. The only explanation, if these are not teeth wounds, is that they are the outline of the area of contact of the shark's rough skin with the body of the victim as he was thrown from the water. This is believed to be the true explanation.

The significance of this was not realised at the time. Not until some years later did it become evident that sharks have other methods of injuring swimmers than with their teeth. It was well illustrated by an unusual incident that happened to James Knight, in a canal near Homebush Bay, Sydney, on Christmas Day 1930.

Knight was swimming in about 2.5 metres of water when he felt a bump on his right hip. He thought he had struck a log, but then he was bumped again more heavily. He decided this was no log—it was a shark. He began churning the water to scare it away. This had no effect, for the shark shot in again and hit him on the right leg about halfway between the knee and ankle. Knight had almost reached the bank from which he had come when he was hit for the fourth time, again on the hip. It was fortunate the shark was only in a bumping mood, for all Knight had to show for the encounter were shock, abrasions to his leg and a stiff hip.

A similar incident occurred on 28 December 1939, when a telegraph linesman, Percy Carroll, was bathing in Cabramatta Creek near the Warwick Farm racecourse bridge. The creek runs off Georges River, Sydney, nearly 50 kilometres from its mouth.

Both these incidents were in inland waters and more or less confined spaces. Incidents similar to that reported by Dr Miller in which swimmers have been attacked at long distances from the shore have also been recorded.

One which was well documented and attracted considerable interest at the time, occurred at Austinmer, a beach south of Sydney, on 14 February 1935, on a warm and sultry midsummer's day. Darcy Lorenz, with five others, was more than 200 metres from shore, waiting in the surf for some big rolling waves to take them "shooting" to the beach. All his friends caught the shoot, but Lorenz missed it. He was left alone. He was sweeping down the slope of the next one, holding on to a pneumatic surfboard, when he felt something brush against his leg.

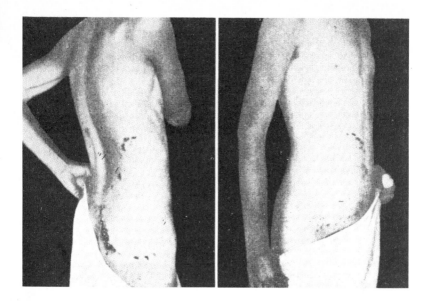

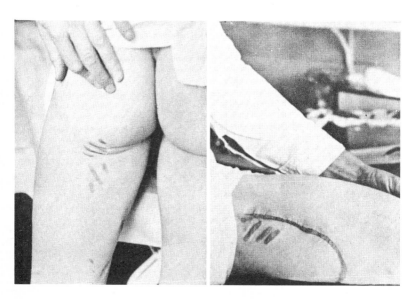

TOP: *A.B.'s wounds at Cleveland Bay. Photograph taken seven days after the attack. The wounds were not deep. They were deepest on the buttock, where the muscles were exposed. Some of the wounds in the chest penetrated as far as the ribs.*

BOTTOM: *Darcy Lorenz's thigh wounds.*

He felt little pain, but when he reached the shore he staggered to his feet and found that he was bleeding profusely from gashes about 15 centimetres long on the inner part of his left thigh. The main vessels of the thigh were bared. Dr Crossle of Bulli, who stitched the wounds, supplied the information and the photographs, which appear in this book. Lorenz made an uninterrupted recovery.

It was generally believed at the time that Lorenz had been injured by a shark, but some expressed the opinion that it might have been a large fish not previously known to attack surfers.

At first sight, in Lorenz's wounds there would appear to be seven teeth marks on the back of the thigh and four on the inner aspect, although they may be brush marks. The J-shaped linear scar on the inner side of the thigh marks the outline of a flap of skin and other tissues torn up by the force of the shark's impact.

The attacks by white sharks on boards and board riders are much more serious and can have fatal results. If a big white shark wants a board rider or human on a small craft, there is no doubt whatever that it will make frightening efforts to gain its food or inflict its warning. The same determination applies to big whaler and tiger sharks. There is a vast difference between the bumping or testing attacks and the attack of a hungry, marauding shark seeking food or sharks of any size in a feeding frenzy.

Recent studies and detailed analysis of attacks indicate that in addition to the bumping attack and the killing and feeding attack, there is another attack pattern. This is known as the "single slash attack", and it makes up between 50 and 75 per cent of the attacks on people. This single bite cuts through skin and flesh, but does not tear tissue free from the body or limb. The shark cuts with its teeth, particularly the upper teeth, but does not lock its jaws and shake to remove flesh. This attack is similar to that made by one shark on another, and the wounds are similar to those found on sharks. Unfortunately, the human body and extremities do not sustain even this form of shark bite.

LOCAL ROGUES AND LONG-RANGE CRUISING SHARKS

An important fact studies have revealed is that one attack on a bather is often the prelude to other attacks in the same area. Places which have been free of attack for years have in many instances become suddenly the scene of two, three or even more attacks within a short interval and within distances varying from no more than a few hundred metres to 15 kilometres. The attacks then cease and the area again enjoys a long period of freedom.

This pattern recurs too often to be a matter of simple coincidence. The theory which best fits the facts and explains the sequences is that each series is the work of a single shark — a rogue shark — which maintains even for years a beat along a limited stretch of shore.

In support of this theory, significant examples can be quoted. In 1922, for instance, there was a series of attacks at Coogee, near Sydney. The first attack was followed by another a month later and two more within the next three years, the four of them within about 2 kilometres of coast.

There are other examples. In 1928 an attack at Bondi, also near Sydney, was followed by another in less than a year, a third a month later (all on the same beach), and within ten days a fourth about 5 kilometres away.

Between 1934 and 1936 there were five attacks on the northern Sydney beaches. To complete the pattern these beaches have been free from attack for years before or after these dates.

In the Georges River, Sydney, on 31 December 1934, two people were attacked about 5 kilometres apart within a period of four hours.

These attack sequences are not limited to Australia. The trail of the rogue shark leads all over the world. A particularly striking example occurred in the West Indies between 1922 and 1925. In five attacks on the beaches of San Juna, Puerto Rico, six people were injured, two of them fatally. The series began on 14 December 1922 with an attack on an American school teacher. Two months later, a Puerto Rican was mutilated. In November the following year the third victim, Professor Winslow, was killed at almost the same spot as the American schoolteacher.

The pattern still continued. In May 1925 — six months later — an American university student was attacked on Condado Beach. The cycle was completed in November 1925 by an attack at Condado Beach in which two people were injured.

There is no concrete proof that these attacks were made by one shark, but the attacks ceased abruptly after November 1925 and no further ones took place in the area for many years.

That a single shark might be responsible for more than one attack was first suggested by Dr William Bryce Orme, port medical officer at Port Said. In 1899 Dr Orme contributed an article to the *British Medical Journal*. He described three attacks on Arab boys at Port Said within the space of a few hours on the morning of 8 August 1899. The first boy, aged 13, was admitted to hospital at 8.30 a.m. An hour later the second victim, aged 19, arrived with lacerations of his forearm and hand. The third boy, aged 9, was brought in at 11.30 a.m. with large portions of the muscles of his back torn away.

Dr Orme said:

> *During 10 years only two other cases have occurred at Port Said, one two years ago, one six years ago. All three boys (as in the two preceding cases) were bathing off the Mediterranean shore, although none was bathing at the same place or at the same time. Many people have expressed the opinion it must have been one shark which bit all three boys and I think this very likely.*

In the descriptions to follow, other instances of this type of attack are given. It is reasonable, however, to concede that there may be variation in the pattern. In a number of instances successive attacks have taken place within a week or two over much longer distances. There are good grounds for believing that long-distance attacks may often be connected and at times occur along the path of a single shark — a cruising rogue shark.

One example of a long-distance succession of attacks, bearing the hallmarks of the cruising rogue shark, comes from northern Papua New Guinea. Here, early in 1931, three casualties occurred on three consecutive days along a stretch of the coastline, some kilometres distant from each other. Another possible example comes from the south part of the same country.

In August 1956 four attacks took place in quick succession near Port Moresby, which might have been the work of a cruising rogue shark. In the first attack, at Fisherman's Island, near Port Moresby, a man was badly mauled. Soon after a Tsira villager had one of his legs torn off while fishing off the reef at Yule Island about 110 kilometres west of the first attack. This man later recovered in Kairuku Hospital. Not long after, yet another fisherman had his leg badly mauled off Paga Point just a few kilometres from Fisherman's Island. The series was completed five days later when a Hula fisherman named Kara was fatally attacked off Fisherman's Island. All the attacks took place within a month.

In a description of the final attack, Kwala Kila, a friend of Kara's said the boy was fishing about 300 metres off the island. Kara screamed. Before Kwala Kila or a third boy with him could move, the shark, estimated at about 4 metres long, sank its teeth into Kara's thigh, tearing away a great mass of flesh. The lower part of the abdomen was also injured and teeth marks were later found on the thigh bone.

Kwala Kila told how he and the third boy had jumped into the water. The other boy grabbed a steel fishing spear and rammed it into the shark's head. They both took hold of Kara and lifted him into the canoe. The dying boy was taken to hospital, but succumbed some hours later.

Kwala said fishermen in the district were normally unafraid of sharks when fishing off reefs. "It is only the one you do not see that kills," he said. "If we can see a shark we know it is all right. No one — not even the two of us who were on guard in the canoe — saw the shark which killed Kara before it moved in to attack."

It is interesting to theorise how many sharks could logically have been responsible for these tragedies. That four separate sharks should attack four different people within a month is improbable. If the number of sharks is reduced to three, it might be suggested that one was responsible for the attack at Fisherman's Island, another for the mauling at Yule Island, 110 kilometres away, and the third for the last two attacks at Fisherman's Island and Paga Point. This is possible. If the number of sharks is reduced to two it might be assumed one tore the man at Yule Island and the second was responsible for the three attacks at Fisherman's Island and Paga Point. This is most likely.

Finally, there could be speculation on the possibility that one shark attacked all the victims. This would suppose the shark attacked at Fisherman's Island, swam to Yule Island, 110 kilometres away, for another attack, then swam back to the scene of its first attack at Fisherman's Island and made two attacks within five days. It then received such serious injuries that if it did not die of wounds it was left with a spear sticking out of its head and was, at least, likely to be discouraged from further attacks. Anyway the attacks ceased.

The theory that some attacks of this kind, taking place about the same time and over distances ranging from 95 to 130 kilometres, may be the work of a long-range rogue, fantastic as it may seem, cannot lightly be dismissed. For instance, on 23 October 1937 a boy, Thomas McDonald, aged 16, was injured off Byron Bay, northern New South Wales, by what was evidently a bump from a large shark. Four days later two men were fatally injured at Coolangatta about 50 kilometres to the north. No other attacks have ever occurred in these areas.

This theory of cruising rogue sharks attacking over long distances might well have been flimsy, were it not for a series of attacks which occurred in July 1916 over a stretch of more than 100 kilometres of coastline along the eastern seaboard of the United States. It is hard to dismiss the claim that these were all the work of one killer and to the theorist they are the classic example of the activity of a long-range cruising rogue.

So serious were the incidents that the entire United States was shocked and the matter was discussed by President Wilson and his Cabinet. What Cabinet considered was one of the most remarkable series of shark attacks in world history. In ten days, attacks occurred along 105 kilometres of the Atlantic coast just below New York, killing four and injuring another.

At the time, it was generally believed in the United States that sharks were harmless. So strong was the disinclination to believe they could be man-killers that after the first attack, two authorities, Dr F. A. Lucas, the director of the American Museum of Natural History, and Dr J. T. Nichols, curator of the fish department at the same museum, both said publicly that there was little danger of a shark attacking anyone. But after the second attack they retracted their statements.

The series of attacks by what was described as the "mad shark" began on 2 July 1916 at Beach Haven, New Jersey, a popular summer resort, about 110 kilometres south of New York and not far from Atlantic City.

A 24-year-old man named Charles Vansant was swimming in about 1.5 metres of water at 5 p.m. There were only a few others with him. The nearest was about 12 metres away. Sheridan Taylor saw Vansant standing alone shoulder deep in the sea. He heard Vansant scream and saw him wildly beat the water. Taylor was almost immobilised for a second. Then he saw the water turn red and rushed towards Vansant. Taylor saw the shark clearly. Its fin and part of its back were well out of the water. Taylor grabbed Vansant, and with the aid of others, who formed a human chain, began pulling him in. The shark came too, its jaws on its victim's leg.

Taylor could have touched it without any effort. They came right in until they stood in about half a metre of water. The shark was still there. Then it turned and made off. On the sand a medical student applied a tourniquet above severe injuries on the man's left leg, but Vansant died a few hours after reaching hospital. This killer, observers said later, was bluish grey and about 3 metres long.

On 6 July, four days later, Charles Bruder lost his life in a similar manner at Spring Lake, 55 kilometres farther north. His right leg was taken off just below the knee and the left leg amputated by the shark's teeth at the ankle. They were horrible injuries, and Bruder died a few minutes after being rescued.

Hundreds of men and women and many children were on the beach on the afternoon when Bruder, far out beyond the outer lifelines, raised a cry for help. Two lifeguards, George White and Chris Anderson, who had been watching the swimmer closely because of his distance from the shore, launched a lifeboat and started for Bruder while the crowd on the beach watched.

As the lifeguards drew near, the water about Bruder was suddenly tinged with red. When White and Anderson reached Bruder, he cried out that a shark had bitten him. He then fainted.

On the beach an attempt was made to bandage his wounds while a doctor was called. Before one arrived, Bruder was dead.

This second attack horrified people in the area. Motorboat patrols were instituted in a number of resorts. Wire-netting enclosures were set up. The entire coastal area went into a kind of systematic and organised panic.

Bruder's death renewed the controversy that had raged for years as to whether a shark would attack a man. It was suggested at the time that a turtle or huge mackerel had killed him. In support of that theory it was pointed out that the victim's legs were torn and chewed as though something had hacked them, and not bitten with the clean, sharp bite supposed to be characteristic of a shark. Colonel W. G. Schauffler, Surgeon-General of the National Guard of New Jersey, and a member of Governor Fielder's staff, who attended Bruder just before his death, described the wounds on the young man's body. Because of the question raised by some as to whether or not Bruder had really been attacked by a shark, Colonel Schauffler's description of the wounds is detailed.

Bruder's right leg, he said, had been taken off so that the bone stuck out to a point halfway between the knee and the ankle. The foot and ankle had been bitten off and were missing. The flesh was ripped as high as the knee, and the bone was denuded of flesh. The left leg had been bitten off at the ankle, the lower ends of the two leg bones protruding from the flesh fully one-third of the length of the leg. There was a very deep circular gash above the left knee, extending down to the bone. On the right side of the abdomen a piece of flesh had been gouged out.

After the attack at Spring Lake experienced surf men and fishermen ridiculed the elaborate precautions taken, asserting that sharks had never been sighted although some small blue-nosed sharks had been caught near the fish pounds at Asbury.

On the other hand, a shark fisherman, T. Hermann Berringer, Jnr, said he believed the increase in the number of fish pounds had attracted more sharks to the area.

This fatality caused the *New York Times,* in an editorial, to say:

> *If the 500 dollars offered some 25 years ago, by Hermann Oelrichs, for proof of an attack by a shark on a living man, were still to be won, claims for it apparently more than plausible would now be coming in from Spring Lake, down on the Jersey coast. To be sure the accounts from there now at hand do not include the statement of any witness who saw a shark ... and tales of exciting happenings off beach resorts are commonly to be accepted with caution. This tale, however, for a time at least, will considerably reduce the profits of a not-too-prosperous season. It certainly was not invented for advertising purposes and unless it was a shark that took off Bruder's leg, what could it have been? ... a reckless imagination might suggest the propeller of a German submarine ...*

Two days after the attack, Captain Frank Claret of the liner *Minnehaha* made a statement. He was astounded, he said, that man-eating sharks had been seen at Jersey beaches. It was the first time he had ever known man-eaters to go north of the Bahamas.

"The best thing to do if a shark comes at you," said Captain Claret, "is to shout as loud as you can and splash the water with your hands and feet." (It might be noted here that the effectiveness of such advice depends entirely on the disposition of the particular shark.)

Reports from incoming steamers supported a theory that man-eaters along the Jersey coast had been driven north by hunger. Skipper of the vessel *Atlantic,* Captain Brewer, said he had seen sharks swimming northward. Off Cape Hatteras his steamer had passed the largest school of sharks he had ever seen. Some were huge.

Of course — it happens everywhere — bathers quickly forgot about sharks. Then on 12 July the nation was galvanised. The rogue shark cycle was completed. On that day a 10-year-old boy and a young man were torn to death by the ravages of a shark. Another youngster was torn from hip to knee by the same monster. It was this third and final tragedy that shook the nation and caused President Wilson to summon his Cabinet to consider the menace.

Early on 12 July, Captain Thomas Cottrell, a retired mariner, saw a dark grey shape swimming rapidly in the shallow waters of Matawan Creek. The creek was only 50 kilometres by sea north of Spring Lake, but it was over 30 kilometres from the ocean. Captain Cottrell recalled the two swimmers killed by sharks on the New Jersey coast. He hurried to town and spread the warning among the 2000 residents that a shark had entered Matawan Creek.

Everywhere they laughed at him. How could a shark get 30 kilometres away from the ocean, swim through Raritan Bay, and enter the shallow creek? Thus the townfolk reasoned, and grown-ups and children flocked to the creek as usual for their daily dip.

But Captain Cottrell was right. That night a body lay in the Long Branch Memorial Hospital, a dead child lay somewhere in the dark water and in St Peter's Hospital, New Brunswick, doctors worked throughout the night maintaining the life of another lad torn about the hip.

It was unfortunate that the first victim, 10-year-old Lester Stilwell, suffered from fits. When he was convulsed in the water and went below the surface, Stanley Fisher, son of the retired commodore of the Savannah Line, assumed the boy had taken a fit and raced to the centre of the creek to his aid. Young Stilwell came to the surface as Fisher approached. The lad screamed and yelled and waved his arms wildly. His body swirled round and round in the water. Fisher was warned it might be a shark. "A shark here?" he said incredulously. "I don't care, anyway. I'm going after that boy."

When he got to the centre of the stream there was no sign of the lad. Fisher dived once, twice. At last he came up with the bloodstained figure in his arms.

He was nearer the opposite shore and struck out in that direction, while Arthur Smith and Joseph Deulew put out in a motorboat to bring him back. Fisher was almost on the shore. When his feet touched bottom, the onlookers heard him utter a cry and saw him throw up his arms. Stilwell's body slipped back into the stream. With another cry, Fisher was dragged after it.

"The shark! The shark!" cried the crowd ashore, and other men sprang into motorboats and started for the spot where Fisher had disappeared. Smith and Deulew were in the lead, but before they overtook him Fisher had risen and dragged himself to the bank, where he collapsed.

Those who reached him found the young man's right leg stripped of flesh from above the hip at the waistline to a point below the knee. He was senseless from shock and pain, but was resuscitated by Dr G. L. Reynolds after Recorder Arthur Van Buskirk had made a tourniquet of rope and staunched the flow of blood from Fisher's frightful wounds.

Fisher said he was in barely a metre of water when the shark grabbed him, and he had had no notion of sharks until that instant. If he had thought of them at all, he said, he had felt himself safe when he got his feet on the bottom. He had felt the nip on his leg, and looking down, had seen the shark clinging to him. Others ashore said they saw the white belly of the shark as it turned to seize him. Fisher was carried across the river and hurried by train to the hospital at Long Branch. He died before he could be carried to the operating table.

At the creek, meantime, dynamite had been procured. Arrangements were being made to detonate it, when a motorboat raced up to the steamboat pier. At the wheel was J. R. Lefferts. In the craft lay 12-year-old John Dunn. With his brother William and several others, he had been swimming off the New Jersey Clay Co. brickyards at Cliffwood, about a kilometre below the spot where Stilwell and Fisher were attacked.

News of the accident had reached the boys and they had hurried from the water. Dunn was the last to leave, and as he drew himself up on the brick company's pier, with his left leg trailing in the water, the shark struck. Its teeth shut over the leg above and below the knee and much of the flesh was torn away. He was taken to a factory nearby, where Dr H. J. Cooley, of Keyport, dressed his wounds, and then by car to St Peter's Hospital, New Brunswick, where the torn leg was amputated. Two days later they found Lester Stilwell's body resting against the shore 100 metres upstream from the place where he was attacked. There were seven wounds, four on the body, two on the left leg and one on the right.

After this tragedy one of the most intensive shark hunts in

history began. Hundreds of hunters scoured the area in boats. They used nets, they laid steel meshes across the creek and they fired thousands of rounds of ammunition into spots where sharks might be hiding. Hourly catches were made and many sharks writhing and threshing were dragged ashore.

Two days later, Michael Schleisser, a taxidermist, caught a 2.5 metre shark off South Amboy, New Jersey, about 6 kilometres north of Raritan Bay. When he opened the shark he found in its stomach a mass of flesh and bones weighing about 7 kilograms. The bones where identified as human. They included portion of a shin bone which apparently belonged to Charles Bruder, who had been attacked nine days previously. Mr Schleisser mounted the skin and placed it on exhibit, where Dr J. T. Nichols, of the American Museum, saw it and positively identified the shark as the great white shark, *Carcharodon carcharias*.

After the capture of this killer, shark attacks ceased. Mr Murphy, of the Brooklyn Museum, and Dr Nichols investigated this remarkable series of tragedies and concluded that Schleisser's shark was a solitary one and the sole attacker of the men and boys.

There was no lack of theories to account for these killings. Some said it was a shark season. Others suggested the brute must have been suffering from a kind of shark rabies like a mad dog. There was another suggestion that owing to the interference with shipping — nobody had forgotten there was a world war on — the sharks missed the food they were used to getting from ocean liners and sought after other victuals. There was a theory that recent naval disasters had given sharks an acquired taste for human flesh.

Whatever the reason, four fatalities and another case of severe injuries testified mutely to the destructive power of a shark in a killing mood.

Natal in South Africa has been the locality of some horrific series of attacks. In 1944, before meshing was introduced, Durban had five attacks within 81 days, and again in 1946, four attacks in 23 days. The Karridene — Margate stretch of coast was the locality for five attacks in 23 days. Winklespruit in 1962 had two attacks in three days. Other attack sequences in 1960-61 and 1963 were over longer stretches of coast.

World ocean currents, showing the cold west coast currents and warm east coast currents.

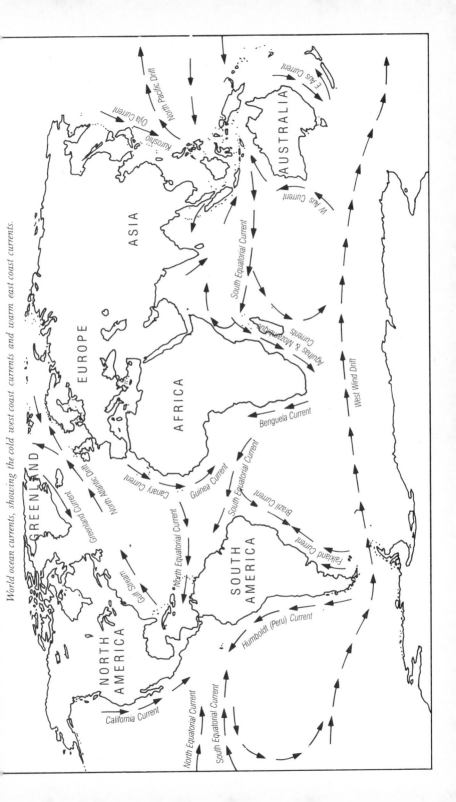

Lifesavers have been attacked during their spectacular surf swimming races. The attacker of Des Wishart at Portsea, Victoria, during a surf race on 4 March 1956, was believed to be a white shark. So too was the shark that took William Black during a surf belt race at Dunedin, New Zealand, on 9 March 1967. After the attack Black's severed surf belt line was pulled in but his body was never recovered. A fellow lifesaver in the race and club members onshore witnessed the determined attack but were powerless to save William Black from the power and savagery unleashed. Another surfboard rider was attacked but escaped although his board was bitten up to an inch in depth near where Leslie Jordan had been killed in 1964. Graham Hitt, one of a group of five spearfishermen at Otago Harbour, Dunedin, was not so lucky. On 10 September 1968 he was attacked while wearing a full black wetsuit in 13°C water. He had been spearing fish 100 metres out to sea from a jetty. The shark was seen by a number of the spearfishermen and seemed to be heading for an attack on them when it changed direction and grabbed Hitt swimming along the surface. It ignored the speared fish on the spearfishermen's floats nearby. The victim died before rescuers could get him ashore.

PART II

SHARK ATTACKS IN AUSTRALIAN WATERS

THE PATTERN IN
SYDNEY WATERS

Australian surfing beaches have few equals, especially along
the eastern coast. Surfers "shoot" the waves with their bodies,
on surfboards, surf skis and kayaks. It is a magnificent sight
to see them speeding shorewards in a foaming mass of swirling
water. Occasional attacks by sharks have not been sufficient to
affect the tremendous popularity of this exhilarating pastime.

Shark attacks in Australian coastal waters have been in-
tensively studied. Dr Coppleson's studies over a period of thirty
years added much to the understanding of shark behaviour and
to our knowledge of the patterns of shark attack. They traced
the influence of sea temperatures on attacks, worked out the
details of the sharks' attack timetable, uncovered the rogue shark
and contributed to the adoption of effective methods of control
and defence. For these reasons special prominence is given in
this book to the Australian attacks.

The first clues to the rogue shark in Australia came from the
Sydney area.

For many years shark attacks were unknown on the Sydney
beaches. It was not until 4 February 1922 that bathers became
shark conscious. Then death struck with suddenness and ferocity.
A young lifesaver, Milton Coughlan, died. His death brought
out the amazing and courageous camaraderie that exists in the
Australian surf.

Coughlan, a member of the Coogee Surf Life Saving Club,
was an exceptionally fine swimmer and an outstanding field
athlete.

There was a surf carnival on Coogee Beach that day.
Coughlan, with some of his mates, was "cracking a few waves".
The lad took a long shoot, but it dropped him in a channel about
40 metres from the beach. The next instant he saw a shark
making towards a bunch of bathers. He shouted a warning.

Almost at the same moment he was struck with such terrific force that he was lifted from the water. Those on the beach watched him struggle. They saw him trying to ward off the shark. They saw the shark snap off his arm. Several lifesavers had raced to his rescue with a lifesaving reel. One of them was Jack Chalmers, who, without waiting to put on a belt, simply tied the line around his waist and dashed into the water. Frank Beaurepaire, an Australian Olympic swimming champion, also swam out to Coughlan. When brought ashore the lad was taken immediately to hospital, but he died shortly after admission.

Nearly a month after Coughlan's death, the blood of another shark victim stained the waters of Coogee Beach. A grim pattern was appearing—a series of attacks in a short time in a restricted area. This time 21-year-old Mervyn Ganno lost his life.

Two years elapsed, then an attack occurred at Bronte, a picturesque little beach about 2 kilometres north of Coogee. Here, at twilight on 13 February 1924, a shark sped in. Within a few seconds 30-year-old Nita Derritt received such serious injuries to her legs that they had subsequently to be amputated. She was more fortunate than the other victims, and made an uninterrupted recovery in St Vincent's Hospital.

Within the next thirteen months the surfers of Sydney regained their lost confidence. It is remarkable how quickly the memory of a shark attack fades. Then on a hot afternoon on 27 March 1925, those cooling themselves in the sea off the ill-fated Coogee Beach heard the shark bell clang its metallic warning.

Jack Dagworthy, aged 16, was in shallow water when he heard the bell but he had little chance to do much, as the attacker literally leapt at him with mouth agape. Despite terrible injuries the boy bashed furiously at his adversary, dragged himself from its powerful jaws and staggered unaided towards the beach. In hospital his leg was amputated. The youngster slowly recovered.

This was the last of the Coogee attacks. The first attack in 1922 had been followed by another a month later and two more within the next two years. The four of them were within a distance of a couple of kilometres.

Because of these attacks, a huge shark-proof net was laid down off Coogee Beach. However, heavy seas continually broke it, and finally the net was dismantled. Sydney experienced three years of shark-free peace, and then the scene shifted to Bondi.

Bondi is a beach with an international reputation. It attracts huge crowds. Since 1919 the people who have surfed in Bondi waters have been estimated by the beach authorities as numbering more than 200 million. For "shooting the breakers" the beach has few equals. Here, in less than a year, two swimmers were killed and another seriously injured. A fourth was killed at Maroubra, 5 kilometres to the south. Three of the attacks were within a period of five weeks. Another grim pattern was appearing.

These were the last attacks at Bondi. But the periods between attacks were becoming shorter. Only ten days after the Bondi attacks, on a dull and cloudy day, Allan Butcher was killed by a shark in heavy surf at Maroubra.

Since these attacks, Bondi has been entirely free of mole-station. But Maroubra has not been so lucky. There was another attack there when 27-year-old Ernest McDonald was fatally mauled by a huge shark on 9 March 1935.

McDonald was pulled from the water by a 16-year-old youth, William Wright, who could not swim. Without a second's hesitation Wright heroically dashed into the water, seized McDonald by the arm and frenziedly pulled the unconscious victim to the shore despite the fact the shark was churning the water only a few feet away.

All these attacks had occurred on Sydney's southern beaches. No attack in living memory had been known on any of the long stretch of beaches north of Sydney Heads, whose jutting headlands form a procession of rocky scenic grandeur from Manly to Palm Beach. These beaches seemed to be charmed, and surfers believed them to be safe.

In January 1934, however, a shark shattered the record and mauled a swimmer with a ferocity that had become tragically familiar on the southern beaches. As though making up for lost time, five attacks took place in quick succession between January 1934 and February 1936.

All these attacks took place north of Manly, the first at Queenscliff on 7 January 1934. On the previous day a 4 metre shark had been seen cruising off the beach. The next day most people had forgotten about it. At 3.30 p.m. on 7 January, Colin Grant, aged 22, a well-known lifesaver, was attacked while well out "looking for waves". The water was slightly discoloured by drainage from the nearby Manly lagoon after recent rains.

While Grant was being assisted ashore, lifesavers with a line rushed out to him. With great presence of mind they tied the line as a tourniquet around his mutilated leg. No doubt this helped to save his life. Grant was taken to Manly District Hospital, where he recovered completely.

The second attack in this cycle occurred two months later at Dee Why, only 3 kilometres away, when a young man, Frank Athol Riley, was torn to death by a shark reported to have been 4 metres long. Lifesavers at Dee Why hunted the killer in a surfboat and although they managed to get it hooked, it broke away. For several hours the beach crowd watched the shark cruise up and down just off the beach.

As happened on the southern beaches, the time between attacks now began to shorten. At North Steyne, only twenty days later, on 1 April, Leon Ritson Hermes was another name added to the growing list of shark fatalities. On this occasion also the water was heavily discoloured by drainage from a nearby lagoon. When attacked, the boy was a long distance from the shore. Although quickly rescued and taken to Manly Hospital, he died soon after admission.

The next season came, and had almost passed, when late in the afternoon of 2 March 1935 — a year later almost to the day and about 10 kilometres north of the previous attack — 22-year-old Herbert McFarlane was killed at North Narrabeen, presumably by a shark which was not sighted. McFarlane was rescued and taken to Manly Hospital but was beyond aid. An outstanding feature of many of these incidents has been the incredible, almost unthinking, courage displayed by rescuers.

Seven days after this attack Ernest McDonald was fatally attacked at Maroubra, 25 kilometres to the south.

The last in the series of attacks on the northern beaches took place a year later, in February 1936, at South Steyne. The victim, David Paton, aged 14, was about 160 metres from the beach when the man-killer struck. He was never seen again. Only a patch of deeply bloodstained water was found.

This was South Steyne's only attack. It was also the last attack on any Sydney surfing beach since meshing was introduced in 1936. But other attacks were occurring in Sydney Harbour, in nearby Botany Bay, and Georges River. Many followed the now familiar grouping of attacks. In Georges River—a short stream running into Botany Bay—three occurred within a year, two within forty-eight hours.

The pattern of attacks around Sydney was now obvious. The inference was that each isolated group of attacks was the work of a single rogue shark. There had been four attacks near Coogee in about three years, three at Bondi in less than a year, and five on the northern Sydney beaches in a little over two years. A group of three attacks had also taken place in Georges River within a year.

This grouping of attacks was not confined to Sydney. Reports from other places gave a similar picture. There was also some evidence that at times the attacks were preceded by the appearance of a shark in the area—usually a large one—which heralded its arrival by acting savagely, snapping fish from lines, tearing nets, and attacking dogs.

With these thoughts in mind Victor Coppleson read with special interest a report in the *Sydney Morning Herald* early in January 1940 that dogs were being attacked in Georges River near Botany Bay.

Because of his convictions he considered writing to the paper a warning that there was a great danger to bathers in the area. However, he delayed. At 10.40 a.m. on 23 January a 13-year-old boy, Maxwell Farrin, was attacked at North Brighton Beach. He was rescued by Sydney Owen, aged 48, but died almost immediately he was brought ashore. There was now little doubt that the shark that killed Maxwell Farrin was the same shark which had taken the dogs, snapped the fishing baits and torn the nets. It had revealed itself as a man-killer. On the rogue shark theory it would strike again.

Coppleson now wrote his letter to the *Sydney Morning Herald*. It was published on 24 January 1940. It stated that attacks on dogs and reports of fish being taken from lines were common preludes to shark attacks on bathers. It advised that special care should be taken in the area to prevent a further tragedy and that if possible the shark should be captured.

The theory was proved almost to the hilt. Just eleven days later death again struck at Brighton-le-Sands, only 400 metres from the scene of the previous attack.

The attacks in the inland waters around Sydney have been

left for special consideration. Besides the attacks in Botany Bay and Georges River already referred to, a young girl lost her life at Como in Georges River on 7 January 1946 and there was a fatal attack at Port Hacking, in January 1927, but most of the inland water attacks near Sydney were in Sydney Harbour and the Parramatta River. In these waters there were ten attacks.

All except two were fatal. Four occurred singly. The others occurred in pairs. In these the pattern of sequences now so familiar was redrawn with almost blueprint similarity.

On the first day of 1915 a man named Tooze was savaged until he died at Sirius Cove. Four years and nine days later, Richard Simpson lost his life at exactly the same spot a few minutes after taking the water. The two attacks probably had nothing in common except their location.

But there is more than a strong suspicion that the next pair of attacks at Bantry Bay, Middle Harbour, in 1942 were made by the same shark. The first was perhaps the most spine-chilling and ghastly attack known in Sydney waters.

On the afternoon of 4 January 1942, a 28-year-old woman, Zita Steadman, was with a motorboat party that was picnicking at Egg Rock, just past Bantry Bay. It was hot that day and just before 3 p.m. the party dived into the water. Two of them stood waist-high. Although Zita Steadman was a little farther out she was still in shallow water. A friend named Burns warned her not to move too far away. She turned to go back then shrieked suddenly. A shark was seen clearly as it churned the water in the attack.

Burns grabbed an oar from a boat and began smashing at the shark. It was attacking repeatedly and with such ferocity that it was throwing itself into the air. The flaying oar made not the slightest impression on it. Gradually it drew Zita Steadman into deeper water.

In desperation, Burns leapt into a rowing boat and tried to ram the enraged shark. This too failed to turn it off, so as he came close he grasped the woman's long black hair as it trailed in the water, and freed the body from the shark's grip. The shark was clearly seen. It must have been very large, as it had bitten her completely in two.

Less than a year later, and only a short distance from where Zita Steadman had lost her life, 15-year-old Denise Burch went

TOP: *Middle Harbour, where Zita Steadman was fatally attacked, 4 January 1942.*

BOTTOM: *Wyargine Point thirty minutes after the attack on John Willis on 17 January 1955. He swam to the rocks in the foreground, where he died. The arrows point to the fins of two sharks still swimming in the area.*

swimming on the morning of 26 December. The circumstances and type of attack were almost identical. She was struck while standing in shallow water, and received such severe injuries to her lower extremities that she was dead when she was taken from the water.

For thirteen years no further attack took place in Sydney Harbour or the Parramatta River. People had forgotten the threat of attack. They bathed unconcernedly in open water from the numerous sandy beaches which line the harbour foreshores.

Then two attacks took place in Middle Harbour within a month and within a few kilometres of each other. These attacks, which received great publicity, are remarkable for the prodigious but unsuccessful efforts made later to annihilate the killer by destroying all sharks in the area.

Details are given elsewhere of the first of these attacks, in which a 3.5 metre shark fatally mauled a 13-year-old boy, John Willis, who was spearfishing off Wyargine Point, Edwards Beach, Balmoral. This occurred about 3 p.m. on 17 January 1955. The boy died during rescue. Scores of fishermen attempted to catch the shark, but although it was seen swimming round it was never hooked.

Three weeks later, at 2 p.m. on 5 February 1955, about 4 kilometres from the site of the previous attack, a German migrant, Bruno Rautenberg, was killed by a large shark at Sugarloaf Bay, Middle Harbour. Rautenberg was a strong swimmer and had often swum across the bay.

The shark was seen by many onlookers. Strenuous but unsuccessful efforts were made to capture it. The hunter became the hunted. Fishing clubs and hundreds of professional fishermen joined in the hunt. The Government shark-meshing contractor laid a 300 metre net across the bay, and a well-known philanthropist, Sir Edward Hallstrom, offered to pay £1000 to the fisherman who captured the shark responsible for the attack. In spite of the reward, the net and the efforts of fishing clubs and innumerable fishermen, no shark answering the description or with human flesh in its stomach was caught. In 1963 a young actress, Marcia Hathaway, was also killed in Sugarloaf Bay. In all there have been nineteen attacks in the inland waters around Sydney: eleven were in Sydney Harbour and Parramatta River, five in Georges River, two in Botany Bay and one at Port Hacking.

The strangest feature of these inland water attacks was that the sharks, for some inexplicable reason, restricted them to a mere six weeks of the year. Of eighteen attacks, all occurred between 2 December and 7 February; six between 25 December and 1 January, ten during the month of January and two between 1 February and 7 February. The only exception to this was an attack in Middle Harbour on 8 December 1916.

A reasonable guess might be that this six weeks is connected with the breeding period or habits of sharks or it is a time when they bring their young into shallow water. Many animals, even some normally docile, are ferocious at such a time. But whether this is so is hard to determine as little is known about the breeding habits and activities of sharks.

Analysis of the Sydney attacks also discloses that, excluding a doubtful attack at Collaroy on 16 December 1929, all ocean beach attacks took place during the first few months of the year; none earlier than 7 January or any later than 14 April.

The obvious answer appears to be that most people bathe at this time of the year, but this is only partially true. Huge crowds throng the Sydney beaches in October, November and particularly December. But no attack on a Sydney ocean beach has ever been reported in these months.

Some observers claim that sharks hibernate during winter and do not become active until January. Others say the sharks around Sydney and Newcastle are ground-feeders for most of the year and only come to the surface in the January–April period, to follow the great schools of mullet, kahawai (salmon) and other fish that sweep along the coast.

But whatever the real cause, there can be little doubt that the reason the sharks have selected the January–April period for their attacks is related in some way to sea temperatures.

Details of sea temperatures at the time of shark attack are difficult to obtain. Early in these studies Victor Coppleson made the observations himself. Other readings were obtained from Mr Roy Tracey, a member of a group of hardy bathers known as the "Icebergs", who braved the water in winter and summer and made daily readings of the sea temperature at the Bronte "bogey hole" as a hobby. These readings, and the readings officially taken in Sydney Harbour, at least gave some general indication of the temperature of the sea in the Sydney area at the time of an attack. These observations indicated that sharks rarely attacked in water below a temperature of about 21°C.

The temperature range covers the wandering migratory movements of all major fish species. Knowledge of the temperature limits of fish and the optimum preferred temperature is used by successful commercial and sports fishermen everywhere. Sharks, of course, overlap considerably in their temperature ranges and while most whaler types and tigers are tropical species, white sharks roam everywhere but are prolific in temperate, even cool, waters. It is the white shark, the most deadly of the killer species, which breaks the normal pattern of shark attacks. Attacks by these sharks in cooler waters outside the accepted critical 21°C zone are more marked as the number of attacks in the accepted temperature zone decreases through the activities of long lining, shark fishing, and, most important, meshing on the swimming beaches. The death of Robert Bartle in August 1967 after being attacked by what was believed to be a white shark in cool waters off the coast of Western Australia is an obvious example of the white shark's divergence from the accepted pattern of shark attacks.

Fatal attacks and attacks generally in Australian waters show a marked decline as well as a shift in locality following the high incidence before the introduction of meshing in New South Wales. In the period of adequate reporting for the twenty years from 1918 to 1937, 57 fatalities were recorded. It took the next forty-eight years for another 57 fatalities to be recorded—a drop of 50 per cent in recorded fatalities.

OTHER ATTACKS
IN NEW SOUTH WALES

Newcastle, 160 kilometres to the north of Sydney, is the second largest centre of population in New South Wales. It has many popular surfing beaches. Since 1919 fourteen swimmers have been attacked by sharks, two in the harbour and thirteen on the beaches.

During the same period attacks in New South Wales outside Sydney and Newcastle totalled twenty-two; the majority of these attacks were on swimmers.

Both of the attacks in Newcastle Harbour were in a small inlet, Throsby Creek. David Miller, aged 12, lost his life there in January 1920. Sixteen years later, on 12 December 1936, George Lundberg, aged 15, was killed at almost the same spot. Several hours earlier a large shark had taken a dog a short distance away at the entrance of the creek — presumably the same shark.

These attacks were typical of what was happening in the Newcastle area. Isolated attacks were occurring, with long intervals between them. This, if it can be called a pattern, was the pattern. There was no sign of the grouping of attacks so evident in Sydney.

On the beaches, too, attacks were sporadic, occurring at long intervals first on one beach, then on another.

The attacks at Merewether and Bar Beaches can be taken as further examples.

At Merewether Beach the first attack took place on 1 March 1927. The victim, Edward Pritchard, was waiting for waves about 50 metres from the shore. It seemed to be an attack from behind, for there was a huge bite in his back. He reached shore with the assistance of a young friend, Thomas Connell. Pritchard spent a long time in hospital, but eventually recovered.

A year later, at Cook's Hill just south of Bar Beach, Edward

Arthur Lane, bathing with two women companions, was fatally mauled. The women heard him cry out and saw him throw up his arms. One of them, Connie Challen, raced towards the beach for help; the other, 21-year-old Lucy Donaldson, with superb courage, swam out to her friend, who was trying desperately to beat off the shark with his hands. When the intrepid woman reached Lane he was on the verge of unconsciousness. She slapped the water and this evidently frightened the shark.

But her task was not finished. Alone with the dying man, she struggled to bring him ashore until two Cook's Hill lifesavers relieved her of her burden. Lane died before he reached hospital.

There was an interval of nearly ten years before the next attack at Bar Beach. Then on 13 February 1937, John Welsh, 32-year-old sports secretary of the Cook's Hill Surf Club, became the victim of one of the most violent attacks in years. The sky was overcast, the tide low and the sea rough. As Welsh had jokingly said on his way to the beach, "a good day for sharks".

Welsh was swimming in broken water about 150 metres from the shore with two other men. Suddenly he was plucked below the surface. The next instant, a great shark threw itself out of the water until about 2 metres of its body was visible. Within a few minutes Welsh's dead body was washed near the shore.

Local residents recalled that nearby a dog had been taken by a shark a few months before.

This was the third fatal attack, but not the last, in this area. Lane had been killed here nine years before, and a sailor had lost his life about thirty-five years previously in almost exactly the same manner.

Shark attacks are easily forgotten, and long periods of immunity between attacks on the Newcastle beaches gave swimmers time to lose their caution. Then again at Bar Beach on 23 January 1949, after an interval of twelve years, one of those attacks which deeply shock a nation took place. Ray Land, aged 20, Northern District surf swimming champion, was torn to death by a huge shark while acting as beltman in a surf carnival. Land's horrified parents saw his final struggle.

Rescue and resuscitation competitions at Australian surf carnivals are usually the main event. A swimmer from each club team is selected to represent a bather in difficulties. He swims to a line of buoys placed several hundred metres from the beach.

TOP: *Wamberal Beach. The search for Noel Langford, March 1955.*

BOTTOM: *Throsby Creek, Newcastle Harbour. The logs where George Lundberg was attacked, 12 December 1936.*

Another member of the team dons a light canvas belt attached by a line to a reel and swims out to "rescue" him. Three other members of the team, with long rhythmic pulls on the line, draw the beltman and his "patient" to the shore, while the "reelman" winds in the line. The "patient" is then laid on the beach and "resuscitated".

On the day Land died, the buoys were 140 metres out, and Land's "patient", Barry McKie, was second to reach the buoys. When only 20 metres from McKie, Land was seen to wave his arms above his head several times, the recognised signal for assistance. He signalled five times before it was realised his line had fouled on a rock and was holding him fast. R. Gazzard, No. 3 linesman for the Newcastle Club, and McKie swam to Land's aid. The three were almost together, when without warning a shark flashed through a wave. McKie turned on his back to avoid it and saw Land begin to swim.

McKie said: "Next thing he shot out of the water. I thought he was struggling with the belt. Then I saw the white body of the shark. It hit him on the leg and he disappeared."

Land was brought ashore aboard a surf ski but died before he could be admitted to Newcastle Hospital. Onlookers said later they plainly saw the shark, which was about 3.5 metres long.

It is interesting to discover that sharks are often seen and have sometimes attacked during carnivals and regattas. One would imagine a surf carnival would appear like bedlam to a shark, with dozens of racing swimmers ploughing through the water together and surfboats and skis cutting about. Rather than attract them, it would seem logical that all this activity would scare them away. Carnivals, regattas and surf races, in fact, appear to attract sharks like dogs to a circus. Many surf clubs have had this experience. Not all the sharks attend to watch the races and special care should be taken.

Land's death caused a public outcry. There were numerous demands for the introduction of meshing, which was proving successful on the Sydney beaches. Although meshing was later introduced, and had been in operation for nearly a year, and nets were actually in use at the time, they did not prevent another attack. This took place at Merewether Beach on 6 December 1951, when Frank Okulich, aged 21, Australian surf ski champion, lost his life.

In defence of meshing, it was said insufficient time had elapsed since its introduction to allow its full effects to be felt. It was also said that the attack occurred in a section of the beach not possible to mesh because of a reef.

On the day Okulich died, he was surfing with three Mere-wether Surf Club members, including 15-year-old James Jones. They were about 100 metres from the beach when the two other lifesavers caught a shoot. Okulich and Jones missed it.

Many on the beach were eye-witnesses of the tragedy. They saw Jones and Okulich waiting together in the distance and watched as Okulich was plucked three times beneath the waves. They saw him surfacing and watched him waving an arm feebly. They saw a dark stain spreading over the water and then the macabre picture of Okulich being lifted by a wave and the sun, shining through the water, silhouetting his body. Along-side him was another dark object. Then the wave turned and the picture vanished.

William Morgan and Ron Galbraith paddled out on surf skis. Although they cruised around for some time, they sighted neither the shark nor Okulich. An hour later his body was washed in by the surf. The shark that had killed him had apparently attacked with great determination, for the body was badly mutilated.

Many dangerous sharks are caught at Newcastle. Since then another incident has occurred at Merewether Beach. It was a typical bumping attack and it occurred on 23 April 1957, later in the season than any previous attack at Newcastle. The victim, Paul Watkin, aged 15, was surfing with twenty other boys about 40 metres out. He missed a shoot, and was alone and off balance when attacked. His wounds were comparatively minor. Although the attack was attributed to a shark, no shark was actually seen.

As in Sydney, the sharks at Newcastle have only attacked for a limited time during the year, but in Newcastle they added an extra month to their timetable. Attacks on the Sydney beaches occurred only between 7 January and 14 April, but one New-castle attack took place on 6 December and another on 23 April.

The only Newcastle attack which did not occur within this period was one on Reginald Ogilvie at Redhead Beach on 31 October 1932. Both the time of the attack and Ogilvie's injuries were unusual. Ogilvie was suddenly hit, full force, by a large

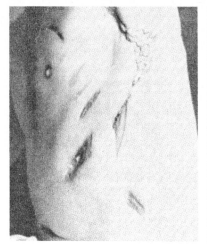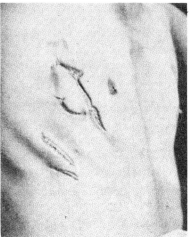

TOP: *The wounds of Reginald Ogilvie in the process of healing. The teeth marks indicate they were made by a shark with prong-like teeth.*

BOTTOM: *The tiger shark which killed Norman Girvan and fatally mauled Jack Brinkley at Coolangatta, on 27 October 1937. Gordon Doniger, left, who was beside Girvan when the shark attacked, and Joe Doniger, right, who brought in Jack Brinkley.*

shark when swimming about 70 metres from the shore. Despite extensive injuries he made his way to the beach and was admitted to Newcastle Hospital, where he eventually recovered. The deep jagged wounds on the front and back of Ogilvie's chest were obviously inflicted by the prong-like teeth of a grey nurse or mako and not by the sharp cutting teeth of a tiger, whaler or white shark. Apparently the shark which seized Ogilvie realised its victim was not its usual target and, perhaps startled, immediately released him.

Away from the populated areas of Sydney and Newcastle, attacks have been rare along the rest of the New South Wales coast. Roughly nine-tenths of all the attacks off New South Wales beaches occurred in the vicinity of the two largest cities, Sydney and Newcastle, and along less than 50 kilometres of coastline.

This indicates that shark attacks are directly related to concentrations of population. But, although it would seem an obvious rule, it is a rule with many exceptions. Indeed, it is not even true of New South Wales. Here the third great concentration of population is in the Wollongong area south of Sydney, comprising Bulli, Thirroul and Austinmer. It includes some of the most popular tourist resorts of Australia. Numbers swimming here are as great as at Newcastle, but attacks on swimmers in this area, with the exception of the minor and dubious attack on David Lorenz at Austinmer, previously described, are almost unknown, although several incidents involving spearfishermen have been reported. The area is one of the shark's favourite spots for attacking boats, while its popularity amongst big game fishermen and the record of their catches provide ample evidence of the presence of numerous and ferocious sharks.

A long stretch of coastline dotted with rivers and innumerable beaches extends north of Sydney to the Queensland border for nearly 800 kilometres. Excluding Newcastle its record is fourteen attacks in fifty years. Three of the attacks were double.

In October 1937 — the month is important — Thomas McDonald, aged 16, was attacked off Byron Bay Beach in the north of New South Wales. The wounds were unusual. They were two or three sets of "teeth marks", one on the upper part of the chest and two on the abdomen. He was not severely injured. Several stitches were inserted and he was allowed to return home,

Only four days later, on 27 October, another attack took place at Kirra Beach, Coolangatta, 60 kilometres north of Byron Bay. This was as tragic as it was unique. It is the first instance in Australia in which two lives were lost in one attack. (Another double fatality occurred near Rabaul, New Britain, when two young girls were killed when swimming with a party of children.) The efforts of the local lifesavers, police and Dr John Birch make this tragedy perhaps the most thoroughly investigated and best-documented of all shark attacks. It was incredibly savage, for in a short space of time late on that afternoon Norman Girvan and Jack Brinkley were both mauled so severely that one died in the water and the other soon after his arm was amputated in hospital.

At 5.30 p.m. on that day there were seven men in a group of swimmers on a sandbank about 200 metres from the beach. Three of them, Norman Girvan, Jack Brinkley and Gordon Doniger, began swimming ashore. They were about 100 metres from the beach when Girvan suddenly cried out.

In his statement later to the police, Gordon Doniger said he and Norman Girvan entered the water together. He swam about 135 metres over a channel to a sandspit. He then took a shoot back about 75 metres towards the shore.

He was then in the channel. Girvan was also there. They joked for a while about sharks. Suddenly Girvan cried out, "Quick, Don, a shark's got me."

He thought Girvan was still joking, but when Girvan put up his arm, blood was everywhere.

Girvan called out, "It won't let me go. It has got my leg." Doniger said that when he reached Girvan, he felt him being shaken forcibly. Girvan was then pulled out of his arms. The shark surfaced. He saw it was a large one. Girvan said, "I'm gone. Goodbye." Almost immediately the shark dragged him under.

Doniger said that as he was swimming over to help Girvan he saw Jack Brinkley nearby. He called to him for help, but just as Brinkley started to swim towards them a shark attacked him.

Meanwhile, on the shore, Joseph Doniger saw these events.

Without hesitation he plunged into the water and swam towards his brother and Girvan. As he swam out he saw Brinkley attacked by a "second shark". He said, "I know there were two sharks because the shark I saw first was bigger than the shark that attacked Brinkley."

Joseph Doniger brought Brinkley ashore. On the way, the shark attacked Brinkley again. It secured him by the left arm just below the shoulder. Doniger said he saw it plainly. It was about 2.5 metres long.

Norman Girvan had disappeared, but portions of his body were later washed ashore. Brinkley was rescued with severe lacerations to his left side and his left arm almost completely torn off. At Coolangatta Hospital he was given blood transfusions and his arm was amputated, but he died soon after.

Determined efforts were made to catch the shark and on the day after the attack a tiger shark, believed to be a female, 3.6 metres long, 1.8 metres in girth and weighing 385 kilograms, was caught. Two other sharks were also seen. A fourth, said to be a grey nurse, was caught later about 350 metres from the beach. It was unlikely this had anything to do with the tragedy.

Dr Birch gave details of the portions of an adult trunk washed ashore. There is little doubt it was part of Girvan. When the tiger shark was opened, its stomach contained portions of arms and legs showing little evidence of digestion. It was possible to identify the right hand as Girvan's from a scar. The wound on Brinkley's left upper arm was as clean as if it had been made with a sharp knife; the wound on the forearm, about 13 centimetres long, was not so clean, but was not ragged.

Dr Birch said: "From the appearance of the wounds and the description of the attack, it would seem the shark struck or bit the arm with the elbow deepest in the centre of the mouth. There was also a clean-cut wound on the right thigh, some deep, rather jagged parallel wounds about half an inch [a centimetre] apart on the thigh and some superficial wounds one to two inches [3 to 5 centimetres] in length on each side of the leg."

Several features of these attacks are particularly interesting. There is the claim by Joseph Doniger that two sharks were concerned. In few attacks on a bather on the Australian coast has it ever been suggested that more than one shark was involved, although sharks in packs often attack whales. There were also reports that several sharks were involved in an attack at Ross Creek, Townsville, Queensland, and there is another description of an attack in the open sea off Cardwell, Queensland, which claims sharks fought in bloodstained water for the body of a man who dived overboard from a launch. Such occurrences appear to be unusual.

Joseph Doniger may have been mistaken. It is possible and more likely that there was only one shark, whose main target was Girvan. As it sped by, its fin and body brushed past Brinkley and hit him with terrific force. There is a parallel for this theory in other attacks, including one on the four Elford brothers in the Maria River, which is mentioned later.

The suggestion has also been made in a previous chapter that the shark which killed Girvan and Brinkley was the same that attacked Thomas McDonald off Byron Bay Beach 60 kilometres to the south four days earlier. The suggestion is not as fantastic as it seems. Cruising rogue sharks appear to have attacked over much longer distances, and it is indeed a strange coincidence that at this time of the year (October) two separate attacks should have taken place so close together in an area where shark attacks before and since have been unknown.

During the next seventeen years there was only one further attack in northern New South Wales. This was in January 1944, when 14-year-old Peter Weir was badly mauled while surfing at Forster.

In 1954 the rogue pattern again made its appearance. In the first attack, on 27 February 1954, Reg Fabrizius was killed at The Entrance, near Gosford. Thirteen months later another swimmer, Noel Langford, met his death at Wamberal, about 15 kilometres away.

In the attack at The Entrance, Reg Fabrizius was swimming alone in the surf at 5.15 p.m. about 150 metres off the beach. He was rescued and brought ashore. Despite numerous blood transfusions, he died in Gosford District Hospital next morning. The water at the time of the attack was sinister. It was muddy, discoloured and flat. There had been recent floods. The sky was overcast. It was a copybook situation for sharks.

A little over a year later the sequence was completed at Wamberal. About the same time in the evening on 9 March 1955, Noel Langford, a tall, well-built member of the Wamberal Surf Club and a strong swimmer, disappeared about 50 metres from the beach. He was undoubtedly taken by a shark. The attack was so swift that Jan Faithorne, who was with him, saw only a smudge of blood where he had been swimming. Efforts to find his body failed, but four days later his swimming costume, badly torn, was washed up about 2 kilometres south of the scene of the killing.

Concerted endeavours on land and sea from dawn to dusk failed to catch the shark. A drum baited with mackerel was anchored overnight but the drum, battered and bearing large teeth marks, drifted ashore, having apparently been towed by the shark against the current. Two hundred and twenty-five litres of bullocks' blood were poured into the water in the hope of attracting the shark but without effect.

Langford was taken directly opposite the channel which had been cut to allow the floodwaters of Wamberal Lake to escape. Sylvia McInerney, who lived near the beach for four years, said that since the lake had been opened swimming had been dangerous and people often saw sharks. Constable Beattie said a professional fisherman from Terrigal, Bill Johnson, told him the coast was teeming with sharks. Some of them were 3 to 6 metres long.

Sharks often swim long distances up rivers and even enter fresh or brackish water. In the period under review, there have been only three attacks in rivers in New South Wales outside Sydney.

One was at Pelican Island, Macleay River, about 22 kilometres below Kempsey. Early on 8 December 1919 James Ridley was enjoying a swim alone when suddenly he was attacked. Although badly bitten about the leg, he reached the shore and clambered up a steep embankment. He lay there for nearly an hour until a passing motorist took him to Kempsey Hospital, where he died the same evening.

In each of two other river attacks, a companion near the victim was injured by the fins or body of the shark as it streaked in to the attack.

On 24 December 1934 at Brisbane Waters, about 2 kilometres from Woy Woy, a Sydney boy, 14-year-old Roy Inman, was fatally attacked by a great shark and his sister injured at the same time. A jetty 3 metres long, near the house where the family was staying, was used by the children for fishing. Throughout the day the boy and his two sisters had been diving into water about 3 metres deep.

Shortly after lunch the children decided to return to the water. Roy and Joyce arrived at the end of the jetty a few minutes before Kathleen and decided to hold a diving competition. Joyce dived first and Roy applauded her. He said he could do better and dived in. As he hit the water his sister screamed in terror.

A black fin cut the water towards her. She kicked. As she did so, something grazed her leg and she felt a sharp stinging pain in her calf. Her brother disappeared in a swirl of foam and she immediately made for the jetty a metre or so away. Their mother watched in horror. Then Kathleen raced to a boat and had almost reached the boy when the shark attacked again, and despite the lad's struggles, dragged him down. Kathleen searched frantically for him but he was never seen again.

The other double attack in a river concerns the four Elford brothers who, one November day in 1947, were swimming and splashing in the brackish waters of the Maria River at Port Macquarie.

The boys were swimming in front of their home at The Hatch, 20 kilometres from the river's mouth. Suddenly, Rupert, aged 13, screamed. There was a swirl of water, and he staggered bleeding towards the shore. Almost immediately there was another high-pitched scream from 12-year-old Edwin, who disappeared below the surface. As soon as he reappeared his elder brother Stanley grabbed him and tried to pull him from the grip of a shark. Suddenly he came free. His leg had been taken off at the knee. On the beach young Edwin died in his brother's arms.

In the meantime Rupert had left the water with blood pouring from a gaping wound with the flesh almost completely stripped from above the knee to 15 centimetres below the kneecap. Rupert recovered from his severe injuries at Port Macquarie Hospital.

There can be little doubt that Edwin Elford was the object of the shark's attack and that his brother, Rupert, was injured by the shark's fin as it rushed towards its victim.

Although Sydney and district meshed beaches with their millions of surfers each summer have been free of attack, an attack on 26 February 1966 at Coledale, an unmeshed beach south of Sydney, captured the public's attention for several reasons, but particularly because of the courage of the victim, 13-year-old Raymond Short, and the tenacity of the attacking shark, a 2.5 metre white shark. After the attack the shark hung on to the boy's badly torn leg until it was in such shallow water that it could be grabbed by the tail and dragged high and dry where it was stunned and beaten to death. Raymond's rescuers, lifesavers Clarrie Taylor and Ray Robinson, could not believe the attacker was still holding on to the lad's leg. One reason for the tenacity exhibited by this small white shark was perhaps the wound which it was carrying along its stomach. Some time in the recent past the shark had been grabbed and torn by a big shark, apparently a big white, before making its escape. These fearsome wounds were partially healed and clearly demonstrated just how tough and hard to kill sharks are, even after being badly, almost unbelievably, cut and torn. Raymond Short, whose courage and cheerfulness did not falter through a long stay in hospital, later presented the jaws of the white shark to the Coledale Surf Club whose members carried out the rescue.

Raymond subsequently made a complete recovery and continued his enjoyment of the warm waters of the New South Wales coast. Like most other attack survivors he showed no evidence of a fanatical desire to avenge the attack and hurt by a senseless vendetta against all sharks. Those who enjoy and are one with the oceans generally accept that the sharks are there as part of nature — certainly a hazard to humans, but recognised and accepted. Vindictive retaliation emerges more often with inexperienced groups, or those who are in conflict with rather than part of the sea.

The attack on Raymond Short and the determination of the white shark attacker highlight the relentlessness of sharks when driven by hunger. This hunger, believed to be severe after the whaler sharks have given birth to their young in estuaries, may account for the ferocity of the New South Wales midsummer estuary attacks. However the statistics compiled and published by US scientist Dr David Baldridge show that hunger is not a factor in the majority of shark attacks on humans.

In New South Wales waters big sharks of all dangerous species are caught regularly by game fishermen and in the mesh nets. Tigers, whalers of all species, white sharks, hammerheads and grey nurses are caught close in while further out these species, plus blue sharks, makos and an occasional thresher, are reminders to Sunday afternoon spectators at weighing stations along the New South Wales coast that big, dangerous sharks are still in their waters. Spearfishermen sometimes brush with the predators, particularly it they have their speared fish suspended near their bodies. Attacks on swimmers are happily now rare but the recommended procedures to swimmers and divers should be followed at all times.

Helicopter and light aircraft flights along the central and southern New South Wales coast have spotted schools of different shark species — whalers, and occasionally tiger sharks and whites. But despite the presence of these shark packs, thankfully, these waters have remained free of injury.

SHARKS IN QUEENSLAND

With the adoption of meshing and the cessation of attacks on the Sydney and Newcastle ocean beaches, attacks in Queensland have come into special prominence. Queensland has a long coastline. Its shark history, apart from the attacks along the Great Barrier Reef, has been centred on four popular swimming areas: Cairns, Townsville, Mackay and southern Queensland. Elsewhere there have been few incidents.

Cairns, in northern Queensland, has three main beaches, Yorkey's Knob, Trinity and Ellis. Shark attacks were once unknown on these beaches. No attacks before 1942 can be recalled by old-timers of the district or by members of the staff of the *Cairns Post* newspaper. If there have been incidents, they are unrecorded.

The first to make shark history in this area was a 24-year-old flying officer of the Royal Australian Air Force, Athol Wearne, who thought little about sharks — people didn't in the Cairns area in those days — and who lost a leg to a shark when he went swimming with a party at Trinity Beach, about 18 kilometres north of Cairns, in September 1942.

This attack was the prelude to five further attacks on the Cairns beaches in the next seven years. There was a break of almost three years, then a shark struck for the second time at Trinity Beach. A young Australian serviceman was mauled to death there on 15 June 1945 only a few metres from the shore. The periods between attacks began to shorten. This time there was only ten months' immunity. On Good Friday, 19 April 1946, a young Cairns man, Robert McAuliffe, was fatally attacked off Trinity Beach.

If a rogue shark was responsible for these attacks, it was becoming impatient. Only four months later Phillip Collin, aged 30, was killed 6 kilometres away at Ellis Beach by a monster, estimated to be about 4 metres long.

There was a lull of about two and a half years. Then on 17

April 1949 a shark struck again at Ellis Beach and Richard Maguire, a boy of 13, lost his life. It was reported that a shark about 3.5 metres long was seen attacking him. To catch it, members of the Cairns Surf Life Saving Club set empty petrol drums with shark lines attached. They caught a 3.3 metre shark near the beach but no human flesh was found inside it.

The final attack of the series happened four months later, on 28 August 1949, at Yorkey's Knob Beach 10 kilometres farther south. A 34-year-old man, James Howard, of Cairns, was the victim. Brian Ware, of Alexandria, Sydney, was on the beach. He dashed into the water and brought Howard ashore, but Howard died in the ambulance on the way to hospital. When the ambulance arrived Ware collapsed. He was admitted to hospital and treated for severe lacerations to his stomach and chest caused by the shark's rough skin and fins as it brushed past him. This was the last attack in the area.

Townsville, the largest city in northern Queensland, is also a popular tourist resort. It lies in a beautiful setting on the shores of Cleveland Bay. Magnetic Island, one of the best known and most delightful of the Great Barrier Reef islands, flanks the Bay. Townsville's record is only three attacks on bathers on its beaches in over fifty years. In the nearby inland Ross River and Ross Creek, however, five attacks have been reported, the last in 1937.

One Townsville attack was unique. It occurred at the ocean baths on Kissing Point Beach on 22 October 1951. It showed that even the "security" of a swimming baths may be false. A shark evidently nosed its way round the supposedly shark-proof safety fence until it found a gap. No one saw the shark, but there is little doubt the victim was dragged through a hole in the fence by a man-killer.

An event of the year at Townsville is the annual swimming contest over the 8 kilometres from Magnetic Island to the mainland. All comers are eligible; men and women, young and old. The organisers take no chances with sharks. Each contestant is protected by swimming in a net supported by oil drums and towed by a launch.

Five other attacks have occurred in this section of the Queensland coast. These were at Mackay and Rockhampton. Two of them were fatal.

A macabre story, which can rank as one of the great mysteries of the sea, had its origin in this area. This is the mysterious death of Dr E. A. Joske, an Adelaide doctor, whose body—disembowelled and with one leg missing—was found early in September 1951 on a deserted luxury yacht in the Fitzroy River near Rockhampton. A shark is believed to have been responsible for this grim event.

Although Brisbane is the largest centre of population in Queensland, and there was a whaling station at Moreton Bay, only five attacks have occurred there in fifty years. On 27 November 1921, Herbert Jack was carrying his son George to a dinghy moored in a metre of water about 3 metres from shore. Just before they reached the dinghy a shark grabbed Herbert Jack's right hip. Jack fought the shark and tried to return to shore. The shark hit again at his right elbow and forearm and right wrist. His son fell or was taken from his father's back. The boy surfaced quickly but then disappeared and was never seen again. A recent attack, which was a double fatality in this same general area, is described in the next chapter.

In one of these incidents a man on a prawning expedition was killed when he dived over the side of a dinghy in Moreton Bay. Another was a minor attack on a fisherman in the Brisbane River 80 kilometres inland in brackish water.

On surfing beaches on the southern Queensland coast between Southport and Coolangatta sharks steered clear of bathers until April 1934, when a comparatively minor attack occurred at Currumbin, about 50 kilometres north of the New South Wales border.

Two years later Kevin Canavan disappeared while bathing off the main beach at Southport. The suggestion was made that he was attacked by a man-eater, but this is questionable. His body was never recovered. Portions of his clothing washed ashore appeared to have been torn by a shark. Four years later, in October 1937, the Coolangatta attack previously described occurred, in which Jack Brinkley and Norman Girvan lost their lives.

The passing of three years restored bathers' lost confidence, then at Southport in January 1940 Douglas Bright, aged 22, one of the State's best lifesavers, swimming about 200 metres from the shore with two others, felt a stinging pain apparently due

to a violent bump as he was going through a wave. He swam
unaided to shore, leaving a trail of blood. The injuries were not
serious.

For ten years there were no further incidents in this area. But
six weeks before Christmas 1950 two attacks occurred in quick
succession. The first was at Burleigh Heads, on 25 November
1950. There had been heavy general rain throughout most of
southern Queensland during the previous week, although the
fall had only been light in this area. The sea was rough. Leo
Ryan, aged 21, was swimming about 150 metres from the shore
when a shark struck him. Gavin Horsley swam out in a belt
and rescued him. Ryan was taken by ambulance to Brisbane
Hospital, where he eventually recovered. He lost a large piece
of his buttocks and two of his right and most of his left-hand
fingers.

Next day, Sunday, the beach was crowded with surfers.
Nothing happened, but at Tallebudgera, a kilometre away, a
shark of about the same size as the one which attacked Ryan
was found lurking under the buoys at a surf carnival. It swam
within 10 metres of some competitors in a rescue and resuscitation competition. They were dragged into a boat and
the carnival was called off.

The following day the shark, a 3 metre one, was again seen.
One of the most intensive anti-shark campaigns in Australian
waters followed. People were being scared away from the
southern Queensland beaches, and the authorities were anxious
to restore their lost confidence.

Fishermen along the coastline began setting baits and lines,
specifically for sharks. On 28 November the new campaign had
its first victory when a 3 metre whaler was hooked. It was believed
to be the shark that had attacked Leo Ryan. On 9 December
the Northcliffe Surf Life Saving Club held its annual carnival.
The club decided to leave nothing to chance. Surf boats carrying
sharp harpoons and surf skis patrolled the beach throughout
the day.

One of Queensland's leading newspaper groups, the *Courier-
Mail* and *Sunday Mail*, decided to provide an aerial shark patrol
for all south coast beaches during the Christmas holidays.

The first test patrol was to begin on 17 December but the
sharks got in first and on 16 December Desmond Quinlan, aged

20, was mauled to death at Palm Beach North, 8 kilometres south of Burleigh Heads, where Leo Ryan was attacked on 25 November. Details of the attack have familiar features.

Quinlan was swimming with a dozen other lifesavers about 35 metres from the shore. A rolling wave approached the men and they all swam to catch it. Quinlan and one of his club-mates, Bill Wilson, missed the wave but the others went planing shorewards. Wilson caught the next wave, leaving Quinlan alone. Wilson was almost on the beach when he looked round to see if Quinlan was with him.

It was then he heard his friend's panic-stricken voice: "Quick! Shark!" Quinlan was struggling furiously in the water. Wilson did not hesitate. He swam powerfully to his friend, but when he arrived Quinlan was on the verge of unconsciousness. Frank Griffin, of Brisbane, joined Wilson, and together they brought the stricken man ashore. It was impossible, however, for him to survive his injuries. He died shortly after they laid him down in the clubhouse.

The campaign against sharks gained impetus. Next day three 3 metre sharks were seen cruising about 30 metres farther out than the spot where Quinlan was attacked. The *Courier-Mail's* plane, with the paper's pictorial editor, Tom Martin, as observer, went on the scheduled test, and in an hour between Coolangatta and Southport Martin saw sharks lurking off practically every beach. In all, he counted twenty-nine. The patrol showed that sharks were moving closer to the beaches. At one beach they were cruising slowly just 55 metres from the shore.

Deputations to Members of Parliament for the introduction of meshing and numerous letters to the press indicated the public alarm. One letter advocated the use of army barges carrying armed servicemen to shoot the sharks. Even more desperate measures to combat the menace were advocated. One newspaper letter-writer said depth charges should be dropped from the patrolling plane. It was then pointed out that while the idea was certainly to kill sharks, there was no intention of annihilating the bathers as well. Also, of course, the small patrol plane had enough difficulties without being asked to drop depth charges.

On Fraser Island, off Maryborough, 800 scouts set grimly to work to rope off their swimming area. Bags of repellents were strung along the ropes at short intervals. An observation tower from which a spotter with binoculars could operate was built. On 22 December the Surf Life Saving Association's State Council decided to seek a deputation to the Government to discuss meshing. The following day a Brisbane firm presented a harpoon gun.

With all these safeguards being taken on the southern beaches, the swimming resorts to the north of Brisbane felt they too should be given some measure of protection, so the RAAF provided a Wirraway plane. Plenty of sharks were seen from the plane, but fortunately they were not in an attacking mood.

Then, apart from a minor incident in 1953, there was a lull in attacks in this area for eight years. In 1958, the sharks again went into action. They made four attacks within a year, two during surf events, one of them fatal.

Attacks then ceased in this area, but in December 1961, two attacks occurred in other Queensland waters which shocked the nation. In these attacks a young man and a girl lost their lives and a young man was seriously injured.

In the first attack, a 22-year-old dental student, John Graydon Garth Andrews, fought for his life against a vicious attack by a 3 metre shark. In water a little more than knee-deep, the shark tore off his left leg above the knee and severely lacerated his left arm.

The attack took place at 6.30 a.m. on 18 December about 300 metres from the shore at Noosa Heads in Laguna Bay, about 140 kilometres north of Brisbane. Andrews had made several runs on his surfboard and was walking ashore, pushing the board in front of him, when the shark suddenly struck.

Horrified onlookers ran to his rescue. The first to reach him were Rawdon Payne, a retired tea planter from Sri Lanka, and Keith Bain. As they pulled him ashore, the shark was clearly seen, lashing half in and half out of the water, only a metre or two away. A doctor arrived quickly on the scene and rendered first-aid. The victim was then taken by ambulance to Nambour Hospital and then transferred to Brisbane General Hospital, where he died about a week later.

The shark cruised up and down the beach after the attack. Lifesavers fired shots at it with a .303 rifle. Lines were set and next day a shark was caught on one of them. When it was slit open the fishermen recovered a human leg. The State Govern-

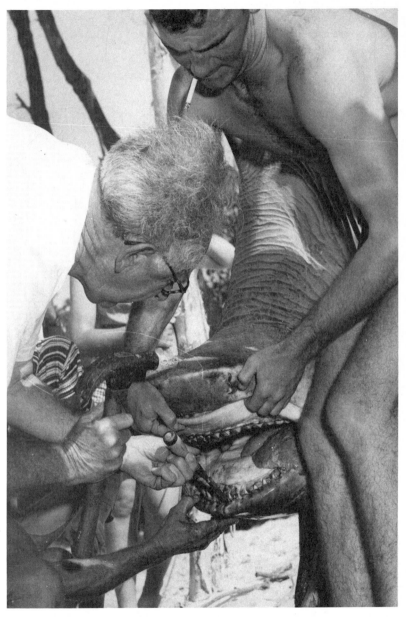

Queensland government ichthyologist T. C. Marshall taking sample teeth from a whaler shark at Noosa. The shark contained remains of a victim.
THE COURIER-MAIL

ment Ichthyologist, Tom Marshall, identified the shark as a whaler.

In the second attack, a 3 metre shark shockingly mauled a young man and an 18-year-old girl as they were frolicking in waist-deep water 5 metres from the shore. The attack took place at Lambert's Beach near Mackay late on the afternoon of 29 December.

The shark suddenly dragged the girl from the man's arms. It tore off her right arm at the shoulder and her left arm above the wrist and savaged her right thigh. It mauled the right hand and wrist of her companion as he tried to drive the shark from the screaming girl. Doctors later amputated the man's hand. The victims were Margaret Hobbs and Martin Steffens, aged 24.

Graham Jorgensen, aged 27, gallantly came to rescue the couple. He raced into the water and dragged them ashore. A trained nurse rendered first-aid on the beach. Margaret Hobbs succumbed to her dreadful injuries; Martin Steffens survived.

Meshing was introduced and proved the success already shown in New South Wales. After initial heavy catches of all dangerous species, the shark population was depleted and the water off all meshed beaches is now incident-free. The early sets on popular beaches proved that the dangerous sharks rarely attacked. One set of the net yielded forty-two sharks, including white sharks, tigers and assorted whaler types. The carnage that these powerful, efficient killers could have wreaked if they had so wished can only be imagined and supports the theory that, in relation to opportunity, attacks are rare indeed.

But although Queensland bathers have been well protected by meshing, two horrifying recent attacks on survivors of boating accidents in the State have reminded Queenslanders that sharks in their waters are a danger that should not be forgotten. These incidents are described later in this book.

SHARKS AND PEARL DIVERS ON THE GREAT BARRIER REEF

Along the eastern border of the Queensland coast for the greater part of its distance, lies the Great Barrier Reef, the finest coral formation in the world, and a famous fishing ground for pearls and pearlshell, bêche-de-mer and trochus. It is one of the commonest sites for shark attacks in Australia.

Most divers seem to have a charmed life so far as sharks are concerned but many have been attacked. The sharks discriminate against certain types of divers. Some divers work in full diving dress, others dive in helmets only. Many, especially the native divers, are naked "swim divers". It is these swim divers that particularly interest the sharks. The sharks show little interest, for instance, in dress divers.

Dress divers usually treat sharks with a certain amount of contempt, for they believe, with ample justification, that sharks will not attack them unless they become the aggressors. It is usual for them to see sharks up to 5.5 metres long on the reef every day. They simply stand motionless until the shark loses interest and moves away. Thousands of dress divers have worked among sharks along the Great Barrier Reef, but if the reports can be believed, only three of them have been attacked over a period of sixty years. In two of these cases the divers were said to have molested the sharks. It is a good working rule for a diver never to take liberties with sharks.

In warmer waters, helmet diving was commonly used. Helmets have in turn been replaced by Scuba and hooka gear. This was introduced by the Japanese, who are expert divers. They discard their heavy dress and obtain greater freedom of movement by diving in helmet and corselet only. In an emergency, a helmet diver can free himself of his equipment but there have been occasions when lugger crews have dragged on the lines only to pull up an empty helmet and corselet for which sharks or gropers have been blamed.

Although no attacks by sharks on helmet divers are known to have occurred along the Great Barrier Reef, the divers take no risks, and when coming to the surface tie their shell bags to their feet to protect them. One helmet diver said he found himself dangling as the centre of attraction for a group of seven huge sharks at about 20 metres. He had no defence and there was nothing he could do. After a brief wait four of the sharks became bored and swam away, but the three remaining ones followed him down to 40 metres, where he again remained motionless until they lazed off.

In 1950 a helmet diver was attacked by a shark at Mangallia Reef, near Touho, on the east coast of New Caledonia, unfortunately losing his arm. The diver was collecting trochus shell on the bottom at a depth of about 8 or 9 metres when he felt something catch his arm. He thought it was one of his friends who was touching him. He felt no pain, but his arm was injured so severely that an amputation was necessary.

There is no scarcity of explanations to account for the comparative freedom of dress and helmet divers from shark attack. One expert will say the bubbles from the diver's helmet frighten sharks away and point out it is a common trick for a diver to scare a shark by aiming a string of bubbles at it from his sleeve. Another school of thought believes it is not the bubbles that frighten the shark but the vibrations in the water produced by the air pump and compressor. One authority has said he has seen sharks dash in terror from the vicinity the moment the air compressor was started. But the story is quite different when the number of attacks on working skindivers in tropical waters is considered.

There is now a renewed demand for natural pearl and trochus shells as well as for farmed pearls and pearl shells. This has caused an increase in the number of boats working the tropical waters with divers using the various types of breathing apparatus as well as free diving. The crews of these boats tend to work throughout the year ignoring the cyclone season when boats and resorts tended to cease operations.

The divers work from luggers which weigh about 17 tonnes.

Five or six luggers under a leading man or captain usually operate together with eight to ten swim divers to each boat. The diving luggers remain in a fairly close group and systematically work over the ground. Shell is collected and brought by a fast boat to the mother ship. A good crew could take about 20 tonnes of shell in a season.

Some valuable information concerning shark attacks on swim divers in the Great Barrier Reef region was collected for Victor Coppleson by Dr R. J. Nimmo, of Torres Strait Hospital, Thursday Island.

Generally, the divers of Australia's northern waters regard sharks as dangerous enemies, although many sharks are timid and cowardly. Divers have often seen sharks watch a stationary bait for several minutes, swim around and away from it and return time and again to make sure there is no danger before taking it. Some divers refuse to enter the water if there is oil on their dress or floating on the surface, as they are convinced oil attracts sharks and infuriates them. Divers rarely fail to see a shark each day. They are particularly liable to encounter them in deep water on the outer side of reefs. The tiger shark they regard as their most aggressive enemy. In shellfishing areas little notice is taken of sharks less than 2 metres long, for the divers believe any good swimmer can best them. However, they treat larger sharks with great respect.

While the divers are at work, a shark lookout is continually kept from the lugger. If a shark is seen approaching an alarm is given and the divers are called from the water. The pearl and trochus men believe the shark whose fin breaks the water is particularly dangerous. These divers, who have had more experience with sharks than most people, have found they are more likely to attack a moving than a stationary object. If the diver is on the surface when a shark is seen cutting the water, he immediately freezes. Then he calls for the dinghy which is always close by. In no circumstances does he attempt to swim, for he has been schooled to believe that if he does, the shark will shoot into the attack, as it fears no moving object in the water.

In one instance, a skindiver known as Young Cobbe, who had dived from a dinghy, saw a shark making towards him. Cobbe decided he could reach the dinghy before the shark got him.

He miscalculated. As his right hand grasped the gunwale of the boat, the shark struck and inflicted a large gash along the whole length of his leg. But for one of the occupants of the boat hitting the shark across the nose, he would have lost his life. Three tiger shark's teeth were later removed from his wounds.

There are two unwritten laws among divers: to keep a constant lookout before and whilst diving and never to turn your back or lose sight of a shark. If the diver is underwater and sees a large shark, he cannot call for aid. He must rely on his own resources in the loneliness of the depths. In these circumstances the diver invariably grabs the edge of the nearest reef to offset even the natural sway of his body caused by the motion of the water. The shark usually swims around for a time and then moves away. When it is out of sight, the diver shoots to the surface and the safety of a waiting dinghy.

If attacked, some divers refuse to turn and flee, and put up what fight they can. They will try to push the shark's nose as it comes in for the kill or frighten it off by ramming the shell bag into its mouth.

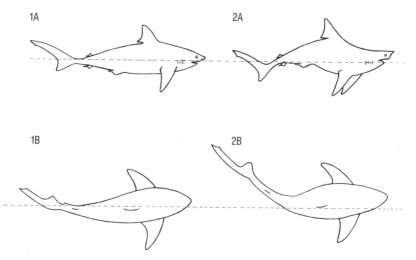

1A and B — Reef Whaler at normal cruising in a smooth and level swimming action.
2A and B — Reef Whaler in aggressive or swimming mode.
2A — Humped back.
2B — Sharp wide jerky swimming action.

It might seem a strange paradox that although attacks appear to be more frequent among these divers, many of their injuries are comparatively slight, and the mortality rate for attacks on divers is lower than for attacks on bathers.

It is significant that nearly all divers who have been admitted to hospital during the last forty years along the Australian coast have recovered, while the mortality rate among bathers has been about 70 per cent. This low mortality rate for divers is in part due to prompt first-aid and rescue by attendant luggers. In the attacks on divers, injuries to the arms, hands and upper parts of the body were twice as common as injuries to the buttocks and lower limbs.

Sharks obviously do not select their victims by the colour of their skins. The divers attacked along the Great Barrier Reef have included Australian Aborigines, Papuans, Torres Strait Islanders and Japanese. This is contrary to the popular belief that sharks will not turn on coloured-skinned people or those wearing dark bathing costumes.

Since 1919, over 70 swim divers have been mauled by sharks in northern Australia and along the Great Barrier Reef. Of 55 instances in which the result is known, 16 succumbed to their injuries and 39 recovered. Undoubtedly many attacks, especially fatal ones, have been unrecorded. Attacks occurred throughout the year, but were twice as common between November and April as between May and October. An unknown factor in this area is the possible attacks on the red-suited Taiwanese poachers who free dive for clam muscle from the once prolific giant clams in Australia's tropical and Great Barrier Reef areas. They understandably do not freely communicate with rescue and medical authorities as they are operating illegally within Australia's 320 kilometre fishing zone.

One diver, Iona Asai, an islander who owes a lot to the gods who protect these people from the terrors of the sea, tells his own story. He was diving from the lugger *San*, which was controlled by the Protector of Aborigines, in just 2.5 metres of water when it happened. He wrote:

On the year 1937, day Friday just about 11 o'clock in the morning, the third time I dive and walked in the bottom. I went behind a little high place. The shark was on the other side. I never saw him and he never saw me. I saw a stone like a pearl shell on the north side and when I turned I saw the shark six feet [2 metres] away from me. He opened his mouth. Already I have no chance of escape from him. Then he came and bite me on the head. He felt it was too strong so he swallow my head and put his teeth round my neck. Then he bite me.

When I felt his teeth go into my flesh I put my hands round his head and squeeze his eyes until he let go me and I make for the boat. The captain pulled me into the boat and I fainted. They got some medicines from the Jervis Island school teacher.

Three weeks after he left hospital he developed a small abscess in his neck which discharged the tooth of a tiger shark. His neck bears two rows of teeth marks and almost 200 stitches were sewn into him to pull the torn flesh into shape. Iona is the local name for Jonah and instead of Jonah and the whale, we can now speak of Iona and the shark. Iona is probably one of the few men on record who have been twice bitten by a shark. About nineteen years earlier he had been attacked and injured off Cairns.

The growth of skindiving and spearfishing activity in Great Barrier Reef waters has not led to any upsurge in shark attacks. This reflects the value of underwater visibility, of watching the sharks, and of better education on safe procedures in known shark waters. An interesting feature associated with the successful black marlin fishery based at Cairns is the number of big tiger sharks found around the outer reefs and shoals. These active oceanic tigers even take whole fish trolled as marlin baits at a speed of four to five knots.

Divers have been attacked by sharks in all depths of water using all types of equipment — hard hats, full suits, corslet and helmet only, scuba, recirculating units and snorkels. Attacks have taken place in a wide range of water temperatures. It is usually the unseen shark rather than one that has been sighted, that attacks. Dr David Baldridge, formerly of the US Navy and now with Dr Perry Gilbert at Mote Marine Laboratory, in his "Shark Attack Against Man", a Program of Data Reduction and Analysis, discloses many interesting data. The number of attacks increases as the years go on but this is to be expected as diving becomes more popular and widespread. Similarly, diver attacks form a growing percentage of all attacks recorded, of the 121 attacks about which information is available, 31 per cent occurred within 1.5 metres of the surface of the water.

ATTACKS ELSEWHERE
IN AUSTRALIA

References in manuscripts, logs and illustrations of Dutch, English and French explorers and their naturalists and artists, show that European man has been aware of the danger from sharks in Australian waters since the explorers' first visits.

The earliest attack documented, a fatality, is listed for an Aboriginal woman in 1791 in the fledgling colony of New South Wales. The French naturalist François Peron, from Nicholas Baudin's expedition, wrote of a shark attack on one of the sailors, M. Lefevre, at Faure Island, Hamelin Harbour, in Western Australia, in March 1803. The Dutch explorer Carstenzonn had commented on the sharks in the waters at Cape York. The English buccaneer explorer William Dampier, in his book *Voyage to New Holland 1699*, published in 1703, commented on the number of sharks up to 11 feet (3 metres) long caught by his crew in a shallow bay he named Shark Bay in Western Australia. In 1837, 12-year-old Alfred Australia Howe was fatally attacked in the Macleay River, 80 kilometres north of Sydney on 17 January. From 1901 to 1968 there were 216 Australian shark attacks, an average of over three a year. One hundred and eighteen swimmers had been attacked, 30 skindivers and 48 pearl divers. Thirteen victims were fishing or prawning, and in seven cases details are not known. Ninety-five (44 per cent) of the attacks were fatal.

Besides these definite instances of attacks by sharks, there were other cases in which swimmers received minor injuries, either from small sharks or from large and unusual fish.

A particularly notable feature of the Australian attacks has been their unequal distribution. If the location of each attack were marked by a dot on a map of Australia, the dots would be thickest along the north-eastern coast and in the vicinity of the larger cities and towns of the mainland. In the period from the start of 1968 to the end of 1986 a further 38 attacks are documented. Of these 16 were fatal including 2 double fatalities following boating accidents.

No fewer than 173 attacks took place in the north-eastern sector between Sydney and Torres Strait and only 43 in the rest of Australia. Only 9 were recorded in northern Australia.

Perhaps the figures should be higher in the great expanse of northern and north-western Australia, but little is known about attacks along this sparsely populated coastline, inhabited mainly by Aborigines. Here, too, the crocodile is as dangerous as the shark. Occasional reports tell of attacks on Aborigines and pearl divers, but the reported attacks are probably only a fraction of those that actually occur. One attack in north-western Australia was of particular interest.

At Broome on 16 May 1949, Mary Passaris, aged 22, had her left forearm snapped off by a shark while bathing. She afterwards recovered in hospital. Baits were set for the shark. Five days later, a 2.75 metre man-eater was landed. It was bluish grey, whitish underneath, had a bluntly rounded snout, and weighed between 160 and 180 kilograms. Its teeth were serrated and triangular in shape. Mr Gilbert Whitley, of the Australian Museum, later identified it from its description and teeth as a whaler. When the shark was opened, the missing arm, showing few signs of digestion or putrefaction, was found in its stomach. A ring on one of the fingers was recovered which Mary Passaris now wears on a finger of her remaining hand. Subsequently, Mrs L. M. Maxwell and Mr L. Pearce were presented by the Governor of Western Australia with high awards for bravery during the rescue.

The main features in this attack are the possibility that the shark was attracted by the flash of the ring on the victim's finger, the lack of digestion of the arm after five days in the shark's stomach, and the recovery of the victim.

A noticeable feature of the attacks in the rest of Australia has been the increasing number of attacks being reported from areas such as Melbourne, Adelaide and Perth, where previously reports from these places were rare. This has been due to the advent of the wetsuit. Surfers, swimmers and divers can now tolerate cooler waters than previously. Examination of the wounds proves many of these attacks are made by white sharks

SHARK ATTACKS IN AUSTRALIAN WATERS 1901–68

	Total number of incidents	Swimming	Spearfishing or skindiving	Pearl or trochus diving	Fishing or prawning	No details	Number of deaths
New South Wales	83	65 (41)	14 (2)	—	4	—	43
Queensland	38	33 (19)	1	—	3 (2)	1 (1)	22
Great Barrier Reef (pearl divers)	55	2 (2)	2 (1)	45 (12)	1 (1)	5	16
Victoria	8	6 (3)	2	—	—	—	3
Bass Strait	2	2	—	—	—	—	—
Tasmania	2	1 (1)	—	—	1	—	1
South Australia	10	3 (2)	6 (1)	—	1	—	3
Western Australia	13	4 (2)	5 (1)	3 (3)	1	—	6
Northern Australia	5	2 (1)	—	—	2	1	1
	216	118 (71)	30 (5)	48 (15)	13 (3)	7 (1)	95

The number of fatal cases is shown in brackets.

A cruising white shark, the temperate-water attacker. RON AND VALERIE TAYLOR

which frequent these waters. If the white shark were a regular seeker of human flesh, however, no one would be able to swim, surf, dive or ride surfboards safely, or even fish in small boats in the southern Australian waters. In the occasional attacks made by this shark, the victim had, in many cases, been released after being bitten once. This has also been the case with attacks by white sharks in Californian and other temperate waters.

In waters of all temperatures spearfishermen have been fiercely attacked when engaged in competition. There has been a series of incidents of this type in South Australia. In the first Jack Evans, spearfishing at Port Hughes on the Yorke Peninsula, South Australia, had a lucky escape when a shark attempted to take the speared fish which were attached to his belt. In another incident, in 1959, Harold Walker and Barry Smith faced a menacing shark "eyeball to eyeball". They were moving back to shore from deep water at the time and fired at the shark from each side without wounding it as the spears bounced off harmlessly. The two men were unhurt.

Then, on 12 March 1960, at Aldinga, 43 kilometres south of Adelaide, Brian Rodger was attacked by a 3.5 metre white pointer which nearly tore his left leg off before releasing it. As the attacking shark spun back to follow up its initial advantage, the courageous Rodger speared it behind the left eye. Although the shark got rid of the spear it moved back to deeper waters and Rodger started his long return to shore, more than a kilometre away. In a rugged, single-handed effort, the badly lacerated spearfisherman used not only his great strength and fitness but his knowledge — gained from first-aid studies — of blood circulation and pressure points. Rodger used the rubber from his now useless speargun as a tourniquet for his leg and headed for safety. As he struggled for the shore he attempted to stave the bleeding from his slashed left arm by controlling the pressure point under the forearm of the injured limb.

Despite his savagely torn arm and leg, Rodger finally reached a small rowing boat carrying two young spearfishermen. One of the lads unhesitatingly leapt overboard and kicked behind to help the rower and lighten the load. Three hours on the operating table and 200 stitches saw the start of Brian Rodger's recovery.

The next attack was on 30 March 1961, when Clyde Buttery was lacerated around the knee when a shark took a speared catch.

Sixteen-year-old Geoffrey Corner was the next to meet a big shark underwater. The meeting took place 200 metres offshore, just 23 kilometres from the attack on Brian Rodger at Aldinga. The date was 10 December 1962.

The shark grabbed Corner on the right leg and, despite being hit on the head by the paddle of the surf ski wielded by Corner's spearfishing companion, Allen Phillips, hung on tenaciously. Eventually the shark let go and the mutilated lad was pulled onto the ski. After a nightmare journey to shore, with the attacker following the ski effortlessly and watchfully, the young spearfisherman was found to be dead. Once again a white shark about 3.5 metres long was identified as the killer.

Aldinga hit the nation's headlines again just twelve months later, when, on 10 December 1963, again during a spear fishing competition, Rodney Fox was ferociously attacked by a white shark only 100 metres from where his friend, Brian Rodger, had been mauled.

After biting, slashing and crushing Fox's chest, the shark

continued to attack, and at one time — in an effort to evade the killer's jaws — Fox threw himself astride the shark's back. Eventually, the shark was diverted by the fish Fox had speared. It grabbed these and made off, towing Fox about 10 metres underwater until the line holding the fish broke. Quick action by a patrolling boat only metres away saved Fox, and after a three-hour operation his wounds were stitched.

Despite the tear in his side, damage to his left lung and upper stomach, and to his arm and hand that were slashed to the bone, Fox recovered in five months and went back to his underwater love of spearfishing and diving for abalone.

After these incidents, Aldinga was closed to spearfishing competition in an effort to write "finish" to the one-sided encounter between man and white shark.

The attack on 3 March 1985 on Mrs Shirley Ann Durdin, diving for scallops at Wiseman's Beach near Port Lincoln, South Australia, was another that could be aligned with a rogue shark theory in that there had previously been three clear warnings of a big white shark in this immediate area. Six weeks before the attack Port Lincoln professional fisherman "Kiwi White had been menaced in his 4 metre runabout by an aggressive shark that chased him as he headed inshore. Four weeks before a white shark of similar size had menaced Ruth and Jim Cribb fishing for whiting in their 6 metre fishing boat at Boston Island near Port Lincoln, and just three weeks previously, schoolgirl Carol Kretschner and a friend had been stalked while rowing in a 4 metre aluminium boat at Deep Bay near where Mrs Durdin was attacked.

The Christmas 1983 attack by a white shark on abalone diver Neil Williams at the Neptune Islands had a happier ending, as he was able to gain safety after a thirty minute life and death struggle in which he finally wedged himself between two rocks while the shark circled. Williams reported, "It took three lunges at me and each time I fended it off with the abalone bag."

Another abalone diver, Terry Manuel, was not so fortunate. In January 1974 a shark returned to the attack four times on Manuel who had been diving for the valuable shellfish. Despite the efforts of John Talbert, Manuel's sheller, coming to his assistance in the boat, the shark kept its death bite on the lower half of Manuel, and only the top half of his body was recovered.

In Victoria, only four attacks were recorded in the eighty years up to 1958 on the thousands of bathers that throng the beaches round Melbourne. Up to 1986 there have been nine non-fatal attacks, mostly with minor injuries, three on swimmers and three on spearfishermen. One of those more seriously injured was underwater photographer Henri Bource, who lost the lower part of his leg while watching seals underwater near the Lady Julia Percy Islands off the west coast of Victoria.

Bource had not been spearfishing, although some of his companions were armed with spearguns. Suddenly a shark, described as a white shark, zoomed in on Henri, grabbed his leg — and kept going. Although he lost his lower leg, Henri today still dives and photographs fish underwater, using a flipper attached to his shortened, wetsuit-covered leg.

Two earlier, fatal, attacks in Victoria are also attributed to the ferocity of the white shark. Both took place when aquatic events were being held. Crowds of onlookers saw the victims in the shark's mouths in deep water a great distance from the shore. Neither body was recovered.

The first of these attacks took place at Middle Brighton, Port Phillip Bay, on 15 February 1930. Interstate dinghy races were being held at 4.30 p.m. when the victim, Norman Clarke, aged 19, dived into deep water off the end of the Middle Brighton pier, about 400 metres from the shore. He was alone in the water. When about 3 metres from the pier, Clarke suddenly threw up his hands, called out and disappeared. He reappeared with a shark gripping him by the leg. Clarke was sitting across the monster's nose hammering it with his hands. He went down again and was seen no more. The shark was clearly sighted by more than a hundred people on the pier. They said it was 5 metres long. One eye-witness saw the shark before it attacked and called out to warn the boy, but the warning came too late.

The other attack was at Portsea Beach, at the entrance to Port Phillip, and the time, 4.45 p.m. on 4 March 1956. A surf carnival had just ended and hundreds of people on the foreshore saw the struggle to the death put up by 26-year-old John Wishart when a huge shark lunged in to the attack.

Wishart was about 230 metres out with five companions. The shark was nearer the shore. As it sped towards its victim, it passed close to two other swimmers. Then Wishart was plucked beneath the surface. Horrified spectators saw him punching frenziedly at the shark. Then, like Clarke, he went down and his body was never recovered.

Differences between these two attacks and those farther north in New South Wales and Queensland suggest a different type of shark was involved. Instead of the tiger or a whaler — blamed for most of the east coast attacks — the shark responsible for these attacks is believed to have been the great white shark or white pointer.

The record of Perth, the capital of Western Australia, is three attacks on swimmers, two of them fatal, an attack on two men prawning, and four on skindivers. These, with four fatal attacks on pearl divers in the north-west and the attack on Mary Passaris at Broome, made up Western Australia's total for sixty-six years until the death of Robert Bartle in 1967.

Up to the time of the attack on Bartle it was believed that Western Australia was at least partially protected from shark attack by the cold current which sweeps up along the coast from the West Wind Drift of the Antarctic.

This illusion of safety because of the colder water was shattered when Robert Bartle, one of Western Australia's best spearfishermen, was torn in two on 19 August 1967 at Jurien Bay on the beautiful, reefy, rugged west coast. Islands in this picturesque bay are populated by a colony of seals and the many reefs offer top line spearfishing. Here, 300 kilometres from Perth, Robert Bartle was spearfishing with a companion some 750 metres offshore when a large shark took him in its mouth about 4 or 5 metres under the surface.

Les Warner, Bartle's companion, fired his speargun and the spear was implanted where Warner reckoned the brain should be. After biting the unfortunate Bartle in half, the predator circled Warner, who on one occasion pushed it away with his empty 1.2 metre speargun. Warner was eventually able to regain the shore and drive for help while the big wounded shark was tangled in float lines and speargun lines.

In a cray boat, *Gay Jan*, skippered by Harry Holmes, Warner returned to the scene where the killer could be seen against the sandy bottom. The speargun was regained and the 115 kilogram breaking strain spear line made fast, but the slide holding the spear line broke free and the killer escaped with the spear firmly embedded in its head.

The white shark has no nictitating membrane but rolls its eye to show the white socket as it attacks. BOB MILLAR

White sharks, some of large size, have been caught in the vicinity of Jurien Bay, but the witness to the attack, Les Warner, spoke of a white membrane, or what seemed to be a white membrane, which moved in a horizontal plane and covered the eye. This was most interesting as white sharks do not have a nictitating membrane although they can roll their eye so it shows white and sometimes do so when attacking with their head out of the water. So an attack that appeared to be a classical white shark attack now has a query after it.

Strenuous efforts were made to catch this killer, with the hunters, Peter Goadby, Harry Holmes, Hugh Edwards and Dr Carl Georgeff, at one stage using 225 kilograms of sperm whale meat. But every tactic proved unsuccessful and the hunt had to be abandoned.

For many years Australians believed that shark attacks in their local waters were confined to a belt whose southernmost limit ran through Bass Strait, about latitude 40° south of the Equator, and that no attack had ever taken place south of this in Tasmania. The matter was the subject of a spirited correspondence in the Sydney and Hobart newspapers in 1934.

According to the opinions of people who should have known,

several reported attacks must have been pure fantasy. "Old inhabitants", shipping identities, yachtsmen, officers of the Sea Fisheries Board and even a Tasmanian Commissioner of Police all said they had no knowledge of an authentic attack in Tasmanian waters. They were supported by police records which in no instance connected a shark with injury to humans.

On 17 January 1959, an attack at Safety Bay, Port Arthur, near Hobart, at latitude 43° south at 4.30 p.m., reminded Australians that sharks strike even in cool waters. Since then there have been another six attacks in the waters of the island state, and two of these have been fatal. The attacks have taken place on both the east and west coasts. Records as far back as the late 1870s referred to sublieutenant Bowyer, of the visiting warship HMS *Clio*, who was said to have been attacked by a shark which bit his canoe in two in the Derwent River. Again in 1880 it was claimed that a man was mauled by a shark at Georges Bay while swimming from a capsized boat; however, this was later refuted by one of the other survivors.

The attack at Safety Bay was the subject of intense investigation, as the island waters were thought to be free from the terror of shark attack. The victim, Brian Derry, a naval rating, was a member of a shallow water diving team attached to HMAS *Cootamundra*. He was attacked several hundred metres from the shore whilst swimming to the ship. Many eyewitnesses on the shore and others who tried to rescue him in a boat saw his attacker at close quarters. They were sure it was a shark.

As sea surface temperatures in southern Tasmania are normally low, ranging usually from about 11° to 17°C, with a mean for January–February of 14.5°C, special inquiry was made to ascertain how far sea temperatures at the time of the incident supported the claim that temperatures of 20°C and over are usually found at the sites of shark attacks. Meteorological reports indicate that both the sea and air temperatures at the time were abnormal. Tasmania was experiencing a heat wave The air temperature in most parts of the State ranged from 32° to 38°C. At Hobart on the day of the attack it was 27°C at 9 a.m., with a maximum for the day of 32°C. Other records indicated that sea temperatures in the area were from 5.5° to 7°C above normal.

Information from the Royal Australian Navy and the Departments of Meteorology in Hobart and Sydney gave local readings and readings from ships in the vicinity varying from 16° to 23°C. The reading at nearby Eaglehawk Neck was 20°C and at Cape Bruny (Weather Bureau) 19.5°C. HMAS *Cootamundra* recorded 18°C throughout the day at 3 metres.

The Deputy Director of the Tasmanian Meteorological Office commented that although some of the data may be conflicting, sea temperatures close to the surface in shallow water probably reached 21°C or higher.

It is also noteworthy that for some days before the attack the Hobart newspapers drew attention to the unusual presence near the Hobart Bridge of large sharks in abnormal numbers and warned bathers specially of the dangers they were running.

If the Australian attacks were to be mapped for each month of the year it would be seen that it is possible to divide the belt into two zones—a tropical zone north of the Tropic of Capricorn in which attacks occur every month of the year, and a seasonal zone extending from the Tropic of Capricorn to Bass Strait (about lat. 40°S) in which almost all attacks take place between November and May.

Based on this information it is possible to mark out a timetable for all latitudes and parts of Australia. The timetable indicates only the danger periods of the year when attacks can be expected. As has already been noted, the number of attacks at any site during the danger period depends on other factors, mainly the population and the numbers bathing or diving in the area and overall weather.

THE TIMETABLE FOR SHARK ATTACKS IN AUSTRALIA

North of the Tropic of Capricorn	*All months of the year*
Southern Queensland	*November–May*
Newcastle	*December–April*
Sydney	*December–April*
Adelaide	*December–March*
Melbourne	*January–March*
Bass Strait and Tasmania	*July–February*

There have been exceptions to this timetable, but attacks fit in generally with remarkable consistency.

But it has been seen that white sharks, the real man-eaters, have put an unknown factor into the attack pattern. Possibly August off Western Australia, December off Adelaide (before the warm water really moves in), and January off Tasmania are also danger months for this killer.

Other patterns are apparent. Bathing and surfing are favoured pastimes of the young. It was not surprising, therefore, to find that two out of every three victims were aged between 12 and 22. But it was unexpected to find twenty men were attacked for every woman. While the explanation might be that the ratio is merely an expression of the fact that men are apt to be more venturesome than women, it is possible that there is some other explanation? Could it be that there is something about women, perfume or something else, which, if not actually shark repellent, might make them less attractive to sharks?

The records also indicate that most attacks occur between 2 p.m. and 6 p.m. Many take place close to the shore, in shallow water. Bathers in a crowd are not immune, although attacks are more common on solitary swimmers. Attacks have occurred in all sorts of weather, on dull and fine days and at high, medium and low tides, in clear and muddy water and even in rivers in brackish water far from the sea.

Attacks take place off most types of beaches. It is remarkable how many reports refer to sandbanks some distance from the shore, separated from the beach by a channel. Many experienced surfers believe this is the formation most likely to attract sharks.

It is common belief that sharks are more likely to attack in calm water, but the condition of the surf apparently has little to do with the matter, for there have been many instances of sharks streaking in on unsuspecting bathers in heavy, agitated seas.

Depth of water has nothing to do with it. There have been attacks in the void-like depths of the Pacific and in water little deeper than a good bath. And distance from the shore? It makes little difference. People have been killed far from the shore and they have been torn just a metre, or less, from the sand. But here there is one important factor. A bather attacked far out has less chance of surviving a severe haemorrhage than a person mauled inshore.

Of 216 attacks in shallow water studied by Dr David Baldridge, who compiled the International Shark Attack file for the US

1am	
2am	
3am	
4am	
5am	
6am	🧍🧍
7am	🧍🧍
8am	🧍🧍
9am	🧍🧍🧍🧍
10am	🧍🧍🧍
11am	🧍🧍🧍🧍🧍🧍
NOON 12	🧍🧍🧍
1pm	🧍🧍🧍🧍🧍🧍🧍🧍🧍
2pm	🧍🧍🧍🧍🧍🧍🧍
3pm	🧍🧍🧍🧍🧍🧍🧍🧍🧍🧍🧍🧍🧍🧍
4pm	🧍🧍🧍🧍🧍🧍🧍🧍🧍🧍🧍🧍🧍🧍🧍
5pm	🧍🧍🧍🧍🧍🧍🧍🧍🧍🧍🧍🧍
6pm	🧍🧍🧍🧍🧍🧍🧍🧍🧍🧍🧍🧍🧍🧍
7pm	🧍🧍🧍🧍
8pm	🧍🧍
9pm	🧍
10pm	
11pm	
MIDNIGHT 12pm	

Times of attack in 106 recorded instances.

Navy, 16 per cent of the victims were in water knee-deep or less, 47 per cent between knee and waist-deep, 31 per cent waist to neck-deep and 6 per cent in water from neck depth to just above the head.

Sharks have actually beached themselves in their attacks and in renewing their attacks.

David Baldridge in his study showed that 54 per cent of attacks at beaches took place within 30 metres of the water's edge, where the majority of bathers would be. Despite the fact that only a small percentage of bathers commonly swam beyond 60 metres from shore, 34 per cent of the beach activity shark attacks have taken place more than 60 metres from shore, supporting the belief that people are indeed more vulnerable further from shore.

Generally victims have been in a small party separated from a crowd or alone. Rarely has a bather been plucked from the middle of a crowd. In fact there has never been an attack in which the crowd in the water exceeded 100 — a small number for a Sydney beach.

Nor is it the first bather to enter the water or the one farthest out who becomes "shark-bait". In one instance there were at least six swimmers farther out to sea than the victim. The victim has often been an expert surfer. The statement, "Several were waiting for a shoot. One failed to catch it and he was attacked by a shark," is common in the description of the surf attacks. It has recurred often enough to be significant.

Recent heavy rain, debris, a swollen creek and an ocean, mixed in practically any proportion, comprise the almost perfect ingredients for a shark lure. The flood refuse washed into the ocean provides succulent food for many hungry marine mouths. It attracts a chain of fish and other sea creatures, beginning with minute sea organisms, each devouring the smaller ones in front, until at the last link in the chain of survival are the ravenous sharks, waiting to pounce on the final victors.

Many of Australia's and South Africa's east coast attacks have occurred near the entrance of creeks and lagoons in muddy water after heavy rain. A noticeable feature of some harbour, river and estuary attacks has been the number of times attacks have taken place immediately after a dive. In two Australian attacks, the victims were swimming to retrieve tennis balls thrown into the water.

HOW SHARKS ATTACK.

Striking first with their lower jaws, sharks tear rather than bite. Their first strike often throws their victims out of the water.

Most injuries to skindivers have been caused by sharks robbing them of fish. Spearfishermen holding fish should never be surprised to find they have a shark for a companion.

Contact with a shark's rough speeding body often leaves a long row of parallel short wounds invariably described as "tooth marks", but the teeth that cause them are the miniature teeth in the shark's skin and not the teeth in its mouth.

One remarkable feature of the attacks is that practically all victims have been rescued. Many victims reached the shore by their own efforts. Some rescuers claim that they actually tore the victim from the shark's mouth. Few, if any, rescuers in Australia have been injured, although some have reached the victim while the shark was still attacking. Certainly others in the water at the time of the attack have been injured by the shark's body or fin, as it streaked towards the victim. There are many instances of astounding heroism of rescuers and dogged determination of victims.

In numerous instances it has been recorded that the shark made two, three or even more attacks on the victim, and that although others were in the water nearby, the shark repeatedly ignored all but the victim. This concentration on the victim and the shark's disregard of rescuers has been a surprising feature of many rescues.

One inference that can reasonably be drawn from the Australian attacks is that, with few exceptions, each attack was made by a single shark acting alone. In very few instances has there been any suggestion that more than one or a pack of sharks was involved.

Most injuries received were on the legs and buttocks, and in many cases the wounds were multiple. Injuries to the forearms, hands and fingers result particularly from attempts by the unfortunate victim to ward off second or third attacks by the shark.

Wounds caused by the actual bite of sharks can usually be recognised. They are either amputations of limbs or ragged curved wounds with lacerated and tooth-scalloped edges with or without loss of tissue. To deduce from the wounds how they were caused requires a clear understanding of the mechanics of shark bite and a realisation that sharks do not bite or swallow the same way as land animals. Fish and other food small enough they swallow whole, but humans, whales and other large prey they attack by tearing off tissue in solid lumps. In their rush at large prey, sharks strike first with the teeth of their lower jaw, then secure the bite with their upper teeth and attempt to drag the bite free, often leaving only one curved jagged wound for the lower jaw with scattered teeth marks representing the upper teeth. In humans, the violence of the drag on the skin and soft tissues is often so great that they split along the lines of cleavage, leaving secondary wounds which appear as cleanly cut as if they were made with a sharp knife.

Not all injuries are due to bites. Often severe lacerations and at times even amputations may be caused by the shark's fins and rough speeding body. The wounds caused by the brush of a shark's body against the victim are characteristic. They usually consist of a line, often 30 to 45 centimetres long, of short parallel skin wounds, each about 2 to 5 centimetres long and 2 centimetres or more apart, which are invariably described as "teeth marks".

Most victims are brought ashore, but many die during rescue or in the ambulance on the way to the hospital. The number of seriously injured victims, with amputated limbs and severe injuries, who were able to make their way unaided towards the shore is remarkable. In some cases, the victims have succumbed to comparatively minor injuries. This is more liable to occur if the attack takes place a long distance from the shore and bleeding continues for some time before rescue.

As many of the attacks take place in isolated places, and the victim has usually to depend on persons with little or no medical knowledge for attention which would try the skill of experienced casualty surgeons, it is not surprising that the mortality has been high. With modern methods there are hopes that the number of attacks and the mortality rate will both be reduced.

Dr David Baldridge, formerly of the US Navy and Smithsonian Institute and now of Mote Marine Laboratory, statistically evaluates all known shark attacks in a paper that has already been referred to. This paper, in common with all works on the world's great marine predators so far, leaves the answers to many questions still unresolved, although it adds greatly to the sum of world knowledge on sharks. The paper also highlights many areas for future research and reporting. Research into reasons for shark attacks, and the finding of a dependable universal repellent, are top priority.

PART III

THE WORLD
PATTERN OF
SHARK ATTACK

THE WORLD BELT OF
SHARK ATTACKS

The distribution of shark attacks is not quite worldwide. But from the United States, the Pacific Islands, and Natal in South Africa, to mention a few places, come many stories of attacks. Not all these attacks are similar to those in Australia.

No Australian sharks, for instance, have ever shown the ferocity of the "mad shark" of New Jersey in July 1916, or of the Colombian sharks at Cartagena in 1951, and there are no freshwater attacks as in Lake Nicaragua.

The World Shark Attack File lists attacks on swimmers from the Adriatic Sea in the north to the South Island of New Zealand in the south. Added to these are mid-ocean attacks on survivors from ship and aircraft accidents, yet many people regard reports and stories of attacks as myths. From other great areas of the rest of the world little or no information has been forthcoming. The reason is not lack of attacks, but lack of reports of them.

Dr Leonard P. Schultz, senior Zoologist of the Smithsonian Institute and custodian of world shark attack files, said, in an interview in *National Geographic Magazine*, that he believed the records of shark attacks to be far from complete. "Far away, primitive people," he said, "do not compile statistics, and seaside resorts don't overwork themselves publicising incidents that could plunge them into bankruptcy."

The majority of known attacks have occurred in Australia, the Pacific Islands, Hawaii, India, South Africa, the Caribbean and the east and west coasts of the United States.

From these places and many other parts of the world have come reports of attacks on swimmers and skindivers, of attacks on boats and injuries to fishermen, whilst stories of attacks on lifeboats, rafts and men swimming in the ocean, the result of aeroplane crashes, shipwreck or falling overboard have been reported from most tropical latitudes especially in the Atlantic, the Indian and the Pacific oceans. In enclosed waters, such as the Mediterranean Sea, where the water is warmer, attacks have been reported at higher latitudes.

Attacks on skindivers have also extended to higher latitudes than attacks on swimmers. On the west coast of the United States, for instance, incidents involving sharks and skindivers have been reported as far north as the Washington and Oregon border, almost as far as Canada.

According to early settlers the Indians claimed that sharks attacked their boats as far north as the Gulf of St Lawrence. They said sharks at times had upset the canoes of hunting Indians and devoured the men. Ballantyne wrote in 1843 that a large shark attacked a small canoe in the Gulf, in which an Indian, his wife and several small children were travelling. The infuriated creature repeatedly attacked the boat. When in danger of sinking, the Indian dropped overboard his youngest child, an infant a few months old, which the shark devoured as the rest of the party made for the shore.

But, at best, only a rough approximation of the extent and outline of the world shark attack belt can be obtained by plotting the locations of attacks—of which too few are known—within lines of latitude. A much more satisfactory result can be obtained indirectly from application of the knowledge that a close and measurable relationship exists between sea temperatures and shark attacks. If it is accepted that this relationship is a major factor in the timing and distribution of shark attacks and that the critical temperature which influences the sharks is about 21°C, it is possible to produce a fairly detailed and accurate outline of a belt, in which the attacks should be expected. The records show that the limit of reported shark attacks is Cape Breton Island (46°N) in the North and Dunedin, New Zealand (45°50′S) in the South. (Since 1964 there have been four shark attacks in New Zealand, three of them at Dunedin.)

Much is known about sea temperatures. They have been carefully studied and recorded by naval authorities, scientists, and navigators. Admiralty and other maps are available which set them out in detail. With this information, it is possible by using isotherms—which are lines denoting sea temperatures—to plot the distribution, variation, and circulation of sea water at various temperatures at different periods of the year. A map drawn in this way, showing the distribution and movement of

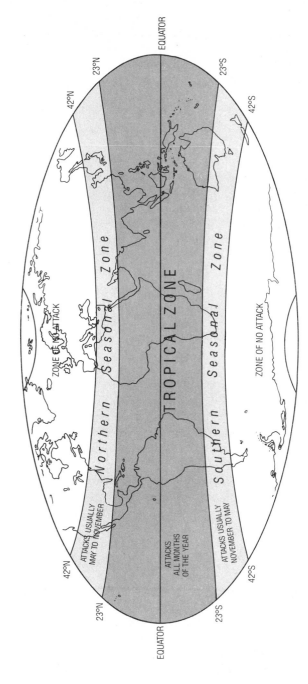

THE WORLD SHARK ATTACK BELT
SHOWING TROPICAL AND SEASONAL ZONES
Zone Limits are approximate

sea water at temperatures of about 21°C, should give a fairly accurate representation of the shark attack belt.

It is true sharks attack in the tropical zone throughout the year, but in the northern and southern seasonal zones, the number and area of their attacks varies each month. For instance, from May to November very few attacks occur in the southern seasonal zone. But during these months, attacks in the northern seasonal zone increase in number and extent until July, when attacks reach their greatest number and most northerly latitude. The attacks then begin to move to more southerly latitudes and to diminish in number. This continues until November when attacks almost cease in the northern seasonal zone.

At this stage as the latitude of attacks continues to move farther south, they begin to increase in the southern seasonal zone. This continues until January, when they reach their greatest number and most southerly latitude. The latitude of attacks then turns north and starts another cycle.

The ocean currents owe their origins to enormous forces built up by wind, sea and the spin of the earth, whirling towards the east great streams of water from the poles. In their eastward passage they meet the west coasts of the continents, where their cold waters are deflected towards the Equator – passing to the left, counter-clockwise, in the Southern Hemisphere, and clockwise to the right in the Northern. At the Equator warm equatorial currents running westwards complete the circle. In their turn they are deflected by the eastern coasts of the continents – clockwise in the Northern Hemisphere, and counter-clockwise in the Southern. Because east coast waters are warmer than those of west coasts, more shark attacks can be expected universally on east coasts and at higher latitudes than on west coasts.

The warm equatorial currents running along the east coasts of the continents are in North America the Gulf Stream, in Africa the Agulhas and Mozambique currents, in South America the Brazil Current, and in Australia the Eastern Australian Current.

Cold polar currents bathing west coasts include the Californian Current of North America and the Benguella Current on the west coast of Africa. In South America the Antarctic Current splits into two at Cape Horn, one arm sweeps along the whole length of the coast of Chile as the Peru or Humboldt Current, the other follows the coast of the Argentine where it is known as the Falkland Current.

The Peru Current brings cold temperatures to Chile. For this reason the incidence of shark attacks in Chile is expected to be low, except for white sharks. No information, however, concerning attacks in this area has been obtainable. The cold Falkland Current on the opposite side of the continent runs along the east coast of the Argentine as far as the Rio de la Plata where it meets the warm Brazil Current from the Equator.

Inquiries in the Argentine show that attacks there are few. There was one at Miramar Beach, Buenos Aires, on 22 January 1954. The victim was 18-year-old Alfredo Aubone. He was rescued. It was reported that a shark's tooth was extracted from a wound in his leg during an operation. It was later identified by Mr W. I. T. Follett, the Curator of Fishes at the Californian Academy of Sciences, San Francisco, as a portion of a tooth of a great white shark.

Beyond vague reports, little is known about shark attacks along the rest of the Atlantic seaboard of South America. Sharks are said to travel many miles up the River Amazon, which lies on the Equator. Attacks undoubtedly occur in Brazil. Farther north in the Caribbean attacks have been reported from most of the islands, including Cuba, Haiti, San Domingo, and Jamaica, details of which are given elsewhere. Some of these appear to have been the work of rogues. In 1930–31, for instance, a series of four took place in the waters around Havana in about a year, which have all the marks of a rogue. Experienced fishermen of Havana believed that one shark was responsible for at least two of the attacks—probably a stray from one of the schools which follow the garbage barges out to sea from Havana Harbour.

Reference has also been made to the series of attacks, possibly also by a rogue shark, on swimmers on the beaches of San Juna, Puerto Rico, between 1922 and 1925 in which six people were killed and injured. There was considerable discussion at the time whether the attacks were by sharks or barracuda. It was agreed, however, that it was unlikely barracuda could have caused wounds of such severity as those reported in several of the attacks.

The victim of the third attack had no doubts about the matter. He said he saw his attacker quite clearly and was positive it was a shark.

In North Atlantic waters the danger zone reaches its greatest expansion in July. At this period the risk of attacks on the United States coast extends north of New York almost as far as Boston. On the opposite side of the Atlantic no information is available to indicate how far north attacks occur on the European coast. The map suggests it should be somewhere on the coast of Portugal or even farther south. Most European countries, including the United Kingdom, are well out of the danger zone. No shark attack has ever been reported from any northern European country, though large and ferocious sharks frequent their waters. Sharks of species generally regarded as man-killers have often been seen off the English coast and in the River Thames. Within recent years big sharks have been captured in the English Channel at Torquay and Pevensey Bay, and also at Filey Bay and a number of other places. Trawlers in the North Sea have been attacked by sharks, which sometimes cause a lot of trouble, tearing nets and smashing fishermen's bones with their tails when dragged aboard the trawlers.

Reference has already been made to the attacks which have been recorded in the Mediterranean nearly as far north as the 45th parallel at Genoa and in the Adriatic. Sharks, it is said, have frequented the Adriatic ever since the Suez Canal was opened, and the harbours of Fiume (lat. 45°20'N) and Pola (lat. 44°52'N) so teem with them that residents no longer dare to bathe in open waters. In July 1954 the London *Times* reported that a Hungarian refugee and a companion set out to swim from Pola towards Fiume. Only one reached safety. He said his companion was eaten by a shark. If this or other incidents could be authenticated they would represent the most northerly known shark attacks. Other attacks in the Mediterranean have been reported from Greece, Port Said, and Tel Aviv.

Little is known about attacks along the Atlantic coast of Equatorial Africa, beyond vague reports of attacks at Lagos, Sierra Leone, and Freetown, the capital of Sierra Leone. Some information about an attack in this region many years ago was given by the Curator of the Old Dartmouth Historical Society and Whaling Museum, Philip F. Purrington. He tells of a tablet at the Seamen's Bethel opposite the "Old Dartmouth". It reads: "Erected by the officers and crew of the Bark *A.R. Tucker* of New Bedford to the memory of Charles H. Petty of Westport, Mass., who died December 14th 1863 in the eighteenth year of his age. His death occurred in nine hours after being bitten by a shark, while bathing near the ship. He was buried by his shipmates on the Island of De Loss near the coast of Africa."

The Rev. Charles S. Thurber reported a conversation with a visitor who was with the crew at the time. The vessel was lying becalmed in hot weather off the African coast and the crew wished to swim. The master talked them out of it. "Sharks," he said. But after supper Petty stole away. He was in the water only a minute. Then he was attacked. A line was thrown out, but by the time he was pulled aboard most of one leg was torn away.

This information was elicited in response to an inquiry concerning reports that the old whaler logs which are stored in the museum contain many similar stories. Purrington says: "I think this is not so. Sharks were a common problem when 'cutting in' and efforts were made to drive them off, but it is not every whaleman who would be as headstrong as Charles Petty."

The tip of Africa reaches only to about the 35th parallel, which is well within the shark belt, and attacks have been reported as far south as Port Elizabeth (lat. 33°58'S) and False Bay.

Farther east, in the Indian Ocean, all waters north of the Equator lie within the tropical zone and most places in the area including Aden (lat. 12°45'N), the Persian Gulf, the Red Sea and some of the Indian rivers have a particularly bad reputation for attacks. Even from the time of the ancient sponge divers it has been customary to write and talk about the ferocity of sharks in the Red Sea. But authentic accounts are hard to find. Stories of attacks in the Persian Gulf are enough to scare most swimmers.

An indication of the number of unreported cases and the frequency of shark bite in this area can be obtained from a statement by Dr Eric Davis, surgeon to the Anglo-Iranian Oil Company, in the *British Journal of Surgery* during 1946. He said: "Nine cases of shark bite have been operated on during the last two years, of which seven were partial or complete amputation of an arm or leg." There are also reports that twenty-seven shark attacks, half of them fatal, occurred between 1941 and 1949 in the Karun River near Ahwaz, about 145 kilometres from the Persian Gulf.

Some tropical areas in the Indian Ocean claim they are free from attacks. In Sri Lanka (lat. 8°N) people who have lived there for years say they have never heard of anyone being taken by sharks. Franco Prosperi, in *Lord of the Sharks*, and other spearfishermen tell of meeting sharks in Sri Lanka without being attacked. The idea that sharks can be scared off by shouting is said to have originated with the pearl divers of Mannar in Sir Lanka who ply their trade amid swarms of sharks. The fishermen about Sri Lanka, however, are the last to admit their sharks are timid. Indeed, they will tell you the creatures are cruel devourers. If the cry *"Mora! Mora!"* is raised, the divers scramble into their boats and wait until the terror passes. But generally sharks have not given much trouble.

The improvement in communications has brought a growth of information about unprovoked shark attacks. Shark attacks are news and when any attack, provoked or unprovoked, occurs there is every probability that it will become front page local news and in turn be reported by the wire services. Before the "shrinking" of the world, as a result of communications and travel, many attacks undoubtedly went unreported and un-noticed except by those involved.

The International Shark Research File lists over 100 separate localities in its data, and New South Wales, Australia, with 137 entries, heads the list numerically. Florida, USA, is second with 107 incidents. Both these localities have the combination of all types of sea water for recreational use, a large number of people using the water, warm water, and a predatory shark population. Another disclosure from the data now available is that attacks are more widespread than was previously considered and there is no doubt that with increased recreational use of the oceans and improved communications the incidence of reported attacks from other areas will proportionately increase. South Africa, and California, North Carolina and New Jersey in the USA are other surprisingly high attack areas.

SHARK ATTACKS IN
EAST AND SOUTH AFRICA

On the east coast of Africa, the Tropic of Capricorn crosses the coast of Mozambique about 800 kilometres north of Durban. To the north are Tanzania, Kenya, Somalia and most of Mozambique; to the east are the islands of Madagascar and Mauritius.

Sharks abound in this region, but the only available information about attacks from thousands of kilometres of lush and tropical coastline has been vague reports from Mombasa in Kenya and sketchy accounts of attacks from Toamasina, Port Louis and Tamarin in Madagascar and Mauritius. For shark information, it qualifies as one of the world's silent areas.

Further south reports from Mozambique tell of attacks at Maputo and Delagoa Bay, of an attack on a child 240 kilometres up the Limpopo River and the pitiful story of the wreck of the steamer *Durao*. When the ship struck a rock in the Zambezi River, passengers and crew took to the boats; most of which overturned and threw the unfortunate occupants into the water. As they swam ashore, sharks attacked them. They killed three passengers and fourteen of the crew. Only the captain, a passenger and two sailors escaped.

Farther south, along the east coast of South Africa from Durban in Natal to False Bay in Cape Province sharks have become a serious problem. In the period from 1886 to 1978, 112 attacks were recorded. In the period up to 1940 there were gaps in the recorded data, so there were probably considerably more attacks than this. Of the 112 recorded attacks, 75 occurred in Natal and 37 in the Cape Province and Transkei.

The story of their attacks along this stretch of over 160 kilometres of coastline and the pattern they followed provides one of the most thought-provoking chapters of this study. Their attacks waxed and waned and moved from one area to another.

From 1940 to 1943 they centred on Amanzimtoti. From 1944 to 1951 Durban became the main scene of their activity. There have been only occasional attacks at Durban since then, but attacks have occurred to the south in the Amanzimtoti, Winklespruit and Margate Uvongo areas and at Umhlanga Rocks to the north of Durban. What is the significance of these concentrated outbursts? Does it indicate some general pattern of shark behaviour or do the sharks follow some natural law?

Statistics are incomplete for attacks in the period 1906 to 1940. There must, however, have been a worrying number of attacks, for in 1907 the Durban Council erected a shark-proof enclosure, which remained in place until it was so badly damaged by the sea that it had to be demolished in 1928. There are, however, data of eleven attacks in Natal Province. Of these, five were in 1940. All were fatal and took place 30 kilometres from Durban at Amanzimtoti and nearby Warner Beach and Winklespruit, a distance of just 8 kilometres. Two years later there was another attack at Umkomaas, 19 kilometres away. After a further attack at Amanzimtoti in 1943 the attacks ceased. It then became the turn of Durban.

Durban, the capital city of Natal, has for years been the premier bathing resort of South Africa and about 150,000 people visit there annually. In nearly forty years — from 1906 to 1944 — only four attacks were recorded on Durban's beaches.

Again there are gaps in records and statistics. Then, in the period 21 March 1943 to 4 January 1951, there were twenty-one attacks, of which seven were fatal. Victor Coppleson is indebted to Mr N. C. Gracie, formerly Honorary General Secretary of the Surf Life Saving Association of South Africa, and Mr A. Kinmont, Durban City Engineer, for considerable information about these attacks.

In general, the pattern of the attacks followed those in Australia. Most of them took place during the months of January, February and March and most bathers were attacked during the afternoon. Many of the incidents occurred during the rainy season when the coastal rivers were in spate, pouring tonnes of sand and silt into the ocean. These include the Umgeni River, which enters the sea just north of Durban. The silt and debris which comes down after inland rain attracts sharks here in their dozens and the tide carries this brown dirty water to the Durban bathing beaches. Attacks generally occurred during the warm weather and the discoloured periods usually corresponded to those of high temperature.

These attacks threatened the popularity of Durban as a tourist resort. The mounting list of casualties worried the local authorities. One expert calculated that in the Indian Ocean outside Durban sharks were present in the concentration of 1900 to the square kilometre. By 1948 the authorities had become so alarmed that they decided to erect a safety bathing enclosure at an estimated cost of $250,000, despite the failure, described later, of a similar enclosure in 1929. Construction of the new enclosure, however, was delayed by successive restrictions on the use of materials and capital expenditure. In January 1951 Mr Gracie wrote acknowledging the receipt of a reprint of a paper Victor Coppleson had published in the *Medical Journal of Australia* in November 1950. The paper set out the theory of the rogue shark and the success of meshing on the ocean beaches round Sydney. According to Mr Gracie, this created "quite a furore in the Durban City Council", and in view of the conclusions set out in the paper the council reconsidered and abandoned the idea of erecting the enclosure. A contract for meshing was let to a local firm and meshing began on 1 March 1952. Systematic meshing in the Durban area has repeated the success already demonstrated along the Australian coast.

The Durban method of meshing differs from that employed in Australia, where nets are laid overnight and removed next day. In Australia all beaches in the area are meshed and each beach has a regular schedule of so many nettings per month. At Durban the nets are strung along 3 kilometres of beaches and are permanent. Only selected beaches are protected. The nets are pulled up twice a week. Torn nets are replaced. The trapped sharks, dead or alive, are hauled on board. This is a round-the-year job, for Durban's sunny winter attracts even greater crowds than the steamy summer. Although maintenance of the nets is expensive it is generally regarded as money well spent.

The effectiveness of the shark mesh nets has also been shown by the reduction in the shark population along the coast. The data from Durban show a decline in the number of sharks taken in mesh nets from 552 in 1952 to 184 in 1953, down to 85 in

1972. Despite the decline in the total number taken in the nets, the numbers of the two most dangerous attacking sharks (whites and tiger) between 1965 and 1975 remained high, with a minimum of 11 white sharks and 15 tigers in any one year, and an annual maximum of 48 white sharks and 37 tigers. In the period 1966 to 1974, the catch from netting of the three most dangerous species was 268 white sharks (2.7%), 198 tiger sharks (2%), and 750 carcharinids — *C. leucas*, the bull or Zambezi shark (10.6% of the total shark catch).

During the time attacks were taking place at Durban, people bathed in relative safety at the numerous resorts on the South Coast. The attacks near Amanzimtoti during 1940-43 were followed by an almost complete lull. Along the whole length of the South Coast there were only three attacks during the next fifteen years. These were at Scottburgh, Winklespruit and Port Edward. At the end of this period the South Coast sharks broke all records for Natal or anywhere else in the world.

At Karridene, on 18 December 1957, a 16-year-old boy was attacked. He lost a leg but recovered. Two days afterwards at Uvongo, about 80 kilometres to the south, another boy, aged 14, was killed almost instantly. Two days later, on 23 December, Vernon Barry lost his life at Margate, 6 kilometres away. One week later, again at Margate, a young woman, Julia Painting, was savagely attacked. She recovered. The sharks did not let up. On 9 January 1958, ten days later, at Scottburgh, a 42-year-old man was attacked and died almost instantly.

These attacks caused general alarm. Flocks of visitors, who were spending their Christmas holidays on the South Coast began packing their bags and checking out of their hotels. There was a widespread call for action. Civic leaders were blamed for not providing sufficient protection for bathers. Predictions were made that if something were not done immediately the South Coast would rapidly degenerate into a string of ghost resorts. The South African Council for Scientific and Industrial Research began collecting information on repellents and other methods of controlling sharks (electrical, sonic, ultrasonic or mechanical). The National Physical Research Laboratory studied likely lines of research. His Honour the Administrator of Natal constituted the Natal Coast Safety Bathing Association under the Chairmanship of Mr R. B. Archibald, MPC, representing all towns and resorts interested in the problem, and charged it specifically with the duty of devising ways and means of combating the menace.

One of the first actions of the authorities was to adopt helicopter patrols for all the main beaches. The duties of the helicopters were to spot sharks, warn bathers, and assist in any rescues. These patrols were first constituted on 9 January 1958 at Durban. Another use of the helicopters was to place in position special lightweight nylon nets, 90 metres long, and later lift them and tow them to the beach for servicing. The nets were rigged to buoys and laid in a square or triangular pattern.

The South African Navy also took a hand. In a two-day attack on the sharks in the Margate-Uvongo area the frigate SAS *Vrystaat*, designed for atomic submarine warfare, dropped twenty-four 45 kilogram depth charges which they detonated in 24 metres of water. Only eight dead sharks were seen. A further thirty-nine charges were dropped with diminishing fatal results to the sharks, owing apparently to a general exodus of sharks and fish from the area. Considerable differences of opinion were expressed concerning the value of these measures. Scientists and others protested that the bombing was more likely to attract sharks than repel them. At Margate ski-boat patrols were instituted and it was proposed that, whenever sharks were spotted, police armed with hand-grenades should man the ski-boats and bombard the area. Another suggestion was to fit sonic vibrators into buoys.

One method of protecting bathers for which great hopes were entertained was the use of a relatively cheap all-metal enclosure, made of water piping and wire meshing. The whole outfit was designed and constructed in Natal and patented. The units forming the enclosure were easy to manhandle into position. They were self-anchoring on a sandy bottom and successfully survived a four months' test including a battering by equinoctial tides.

After these bodies went into action, there was a lull of only three months. On 3 April 1958, a skindiver was killed at unmeshed Port Edward. He and his two companions had been swimming in shoulder-depth water and his two companions caught a wave to shore. The victim, Baden Horst, was attacked twice and lost both arms, his right leg and part of his torso.

Two days later at Uvongo, north along the coast, there was another fatal attack. The local council took advantage of the low spring tides to try to repair their damaged shark-proof enclosure. Mrs Fay Bester, holidaying with her four children, was part of a group standing knee-deep at the river mouth watching the work. A shark came out of the river channel, knocked Mrs Bester into the water, grabbed her again about the middle and after much shaking bit her almost in two. Subsequently all the resorts, with the exception of Port Edward, were provided with some form of protection.

Since then Durban has completed ten successive years free from attacks, but along the southern beaches the sharks intensified their onslaughts. Here in less than three years, they increased their score by a further eight attacks; three in the Amanzimtoti area in less than a year and within a distance of 8 kilometres. They tore off a boy's leg at Port Shepstone and killed a bather swimming outside a safety fence at Margate.

Farther south, in Cape Province, usually comparatively free from attacks, sharks killed a 15-year-old boy at East London, menaced a spearfisherman at Port Elizabeth and attacked a boy aged 18 at Melkbaii in the Strand just south of Cape Town.

This long and tragic succession of calamities spread fear and alarm throughout the country. For years, Natal's South Coast had been South Africa's playground and favourite summer resort. People began to steer clear of the area. Hotel keepers, flat owners and town councillors became increasingly worried with every attack. The local people and municipal organisations tried to do what they could. Some erected enclosures. These were promptly destroyed by storms and wild weather.

Amidst these events, the continued immunity of Durban stood out conspicuously. Its seemingly miraculous exemption highlighted the effectiveness of the meshing introduced by the Durban City Council in 1952. With this strikingly successful example at hand, the South Coast resorts naturally turned to nets for their salvation.

Nets were put down at Uvongo. Amanzimtoti spent $8000 on various shark-netting schemes. Scottburgh evolved nets from the steel rope type of net so successfully used at Uvongo. The Durban City Council, itself, invested in a new shark-meshing vessel.

Unlike the Australian system of meshing, the system used in South Africa is to leave the nets permanently in position. With this method, the durability of the material used in constructing the nets is important. Steel, often in rings, has generally been favoured. Nylon nets as used at Aden and elsewhere have also been tried.

The demand for offshore shark meshing is naturally growing, but shark meshing and nets are expensive. The Amanzimtoti Town Council, for instance, spent $16,000 on nets in two years, only to have them washed away by heavy seas. As usual in matters of this kind there has been considerable discussion concerning the responsibility for the provision of finance. The local authorities claim that the cost involved is too heavy for local organisations and that much of it should be borne by national and provincial governments.

Also, as a result of the public anxiety, an anti-shark campaign was launched to fight the menace and extend Durban's net system to almost every popular resort along the coast. Organised by the *Argus* group of newspapers, the Anti-Shark Research Action Committee aimed to raise $100,000.

In 1964, the Natal Anti-Shark Measures Board was established as the statutory organisation responsible for swimmer protection in the Province. The Board is responsible for all beach shark meshing other than the 25 nets protecting the Durban beaches. The Board instals and maintains 263 nets on the 39 Natal beaches along 275 kilometres of coast. The number of nets used at each location depends on the beach configuration. Experience has shown that 23 nets are necessary at Amanzimtoti beach to give the necessary overlapping protection. The nets are set about 400 metres from shore in two rows about 20 metres apart.

The South African Council for Scientific and Industrial Research, a semi-governmental organisation, has been called in too and has organised a team to investigate the best methods of protection. One of its steps has been to undertake an investigation of the reactions of sharks generally to electrical stimuli and to study electrical barriers as a means of protection.

Meanwhile, the Oceanographic Research Institute of the South African Association for Marine Biological Research, built a large experimental tank on the lines of the marinelands of the United States for the purpose of making a thorough investigation of the biology, behaviour, life history and character of sharks, about which so little is known.

The Institute is part of a scheme for financing marine research, which the Association developed from small beginnings and meagre resources in 1947, to a major project that has attracted worldwide attention. The scheme was to combine a Marineland Aquarium with an Oceanographic Research Institute and a Marine Research Unit. All the profits of the Aquarium are used to finance the Oceanographic Research Institute, whilst the South African Council for Scientific and Industrial Research provides the funds for the operation of the Marine Research Unit. These funds are administered by the University of Natal. The Marineland Aquarium in its first two years attracted over a million visitors.

The Institute began a survey in 1959 of the sharks in South African waters and has carried out extensive work on the behaviour of captive sharks and their reactions to sonic and supersonic sound, and is also investigating every attack. A study of the bacteriology of sharks' mouths has revealed the presence of highly virulent organisms in their teeth and mouths. These organisms are insensitive to penicillin but fortunately can be controlled by other antibiotics such as chloromycetin and terramycin.

In investigations of this kind, naturally one of the first objectives is to identify the species of attacking sharks. Until recently, this had been based on speculation rather than observation.

Identifying the species of attacking sharks is not easy. Under certain circumstances, finding missing portions of a victim inside a shark's stomach may be accepted as presumptive evidence, but the most positive proof is provided by finding portions of the shark's teeth in the victim's wounds. In an issue of the *South African Medical Journal*, Dr G. D. Campbell, Dr David H. Davies and Mr Arthur Copley, a Durban surgeon, in a joint paper, described an attempt to identify a shark's species from the configuration of the victim's wounds.

At 3.30 p.m. on 30 April 1960, the victim, Michael Hely, aged 16 years, was swimming in slightly murky water at Inyoni Rocks near Amanzimtoti in Natal. He was wearing yellow and red bathing trunks and had a silver ring on his right hand. The day was overcast. The sea temperature was 21°C.

While treading water, 10 metres from the shore in a channel 3 metres deep, he felt something, as he described it, "touch his leg". Immediately he felt a pull on his right arm and was dragged beneath the surface. He broke free and struggled ashore. Eye-witnesses estimated the shark to be about 2 metres long.

Bleeding freely, the victim was carried to the lifesavers' hut. Here he was seen soon by a doctor who treated him for shock and gave him an intravenous injection of morphia. After receiving this treatment, he was kept in the hut until he had begun to show signs of recovery. He was then taken by ambulance to the Addington Hospital in Durban, where he was immediately treated for shock and given massive blood transfusions.

The victim's injuries were extensive; in most circumstances they would have proved rapidly fatal. They included injuries to his right leg, right forearm and hand and to a finger of his left hand. There was a large wound on his right flank with considerable loss of skin and another on the wall of the abdomen. The bowel and right kidney were exposed with perforation and tearing of the bowel. A large part of the right side of the wall of the abdomen was missing and the bone of the hip had been grooved by the shark's teeth. At the Addington Hospital in Durban, restorative measures were continued and later an operation was performed. The patient's recovery from these terrible injuries reflects great credit on Natal's first-aid arrangements, the skill of the surgeon and the attention of the staff at Addington Hospital.

In an effort to try to define the attacking species researchers obtained bite patterns of three suspected sharks, the ragged-toothed shark (*Eugomphodus taurus*), the Zambezi bull shark (*Carcharinus leucas*) and the blackfin (*C. limbatus*), for comparison with the wounds by pressing dried specimens of jaws and teeth of these sharks forcibly into simulated limbs covered with paper.

Dr Davies and his team laid the blame for the attack on the Zambezi bull shark (a whaler type), and this again agreed with Australian experiences of whalers as being proven attackers in similar environment and conditions.

A later attack, in which a bather was killed at Margate, provided definite evidence of the attacking shark's identity. Two of its teeth recovered from the wounds of the victim were identified by Dr David Davies, Director of Durban's Oceanic Research Institute, as belonging to the Zambezi bull shark species. This supported the previously expressed view of Professor J. B. L. Smith of Rhodes University that this shark, also known locally as the shovel-nosed grey shark, was the shark most likely to be responsible for attacks in this area.

Analysis of the South African attacks reveals a number of features which are strikingly similar to the Australian experience. The most noteworthy is the dramatic reduction in shark attacks after the introduction of meshing. This is matched by the long period of freedom from attack of the Sydney ocean beaches after meshing was introduced in 1937.

Perhaps the most surprising feature of the Durban attacks is the small proportion of fatalities — only 6 in 22 attacks. Many of the non-fatal attacks were undoubtedly bumps and single slash attacks. In several instances only one foot of the swimmer was injured and other injuries were of a comparatively minor nature on lower parts of legs and feet. Two attacks of this type occurred on the same day.

The sequence of two fatal attacks which occurred within fourteen days in 1944 and the three fatal attacks within a year in 1950–51 may well have been the work of rogues. Other clusters were the 20 attacks near Amanzimtoti between 1940 and 1975, including 5 between 7 January 1974 and 23 February 1975 (4 of these in the brief period between January and April 1974), and the 8 attacks between 1957 and 1962 in the Margate, Uvongo and Port Edward area.

Five attacks occurred between 7 January 1974 and 23 February 1975 at Amanzimtoti, despite the presence of the mesh nets. Study of the graphic report in Tim Wallett's "Shark Attack and Treatment of Victims in Southern African Waters" reveals a story of human courage and the effectiveness of the on-beach Feinberg medical kit and treatment procedures. The report on the attacks shows that beach conditions with a gutter or channel, and the turbid water were constant factors in all five attacks.

The first attack in the sequence was 7 January 1974, when 33-year-old Cornelius Pyper, a lifesaver, was swimming only 100 metres from shore. He "suddenly felt this enormous pressure on my knee and a powerful force thrust me backwards". Pyper punched with all his strength and the shark released him. He swam for the beach with three severe gashes on his right leg.

There he applied pressure to the femoral artery, and other lifesavers came to his assistance with the shark attack kit. Pyper recovered completely.

The second attack was on 13 February 1974 on 14-year-old Damon Kendrick, who with his friend Joe Kool decided to wash the sand from himself after training for lifesaving on the beach. They enjoyed a few wave rides in the close inshore break, even though the beach was closed for surfing because of the murky water and because the nets had not been serviced for several days. Suddenly Joe Kool was bumped, apparently by a shark, and he shouted a warning as the shark savaged Kendrick on his right leg. The shark let go and both boys reached the beach. Kendrick survived the attack, but his calf muscle was badly cut and his right leg had to be amputated below the knee.

Twenty-one year old surfboard rider James Gurr was the third in the Amanzimtoti Beach attack sequence. On 21 March he was surfing 50 metres from shore. As in the two previous attacks, a channel had formed close to the shore and there was a shore break. Gurr saw the shark's fin homing in on him. He lifted his legs and the shark hit the board, tipping it over and dumping him into the water. Gurr swam back the 2 metres that separated him from his board and turned it the right way. As he was about to clamber back on the board, Gurr said, "A violent shove pushed me sideways, and simultaneously I felt the shark against my chest and under my arm." Despite quite understandable panic, he began paddling for shore and then "without warning there was a terrific jolt" and he was back in the water. Gurr remounted his board and again headed for shore while the shark zig-zagged in front of him. Then, as he said, "If it was possible, my fear increased as a broken wave overtook me and pushed me over the shark. I paddled into the shore break, which dumped me onto the sand. As I landed I didn't stop, I just kept running onto the beach." The shark had bitten the surfboard as it had pushed him sideways, and the imprint of its teeth was left in the fibreglass.

On 4 April 1974 another board rider, 17-year-old Anthony Baker, was the fourth to be attacked. Again the beach had been closed to swimming as conditions were similar to those of the previous attacks. Anthony was board surfing with his brother Raymond 50 metres off shore when he felt a tug at his foot;

"it felt warm". Aware of the other attacks, he realised he had been bitten by a shark as his blood coloured the water. Anthony yelled a warning to his brother and rode a wave to shore. He had a deep cut on his right foot that required nineteen stitches, and as was the case with James Gurr, Anthony was fortunate that only some mutilation and cutting had taken place.

Bretton Jones, the victim of the fifth attack, on 23 February 1975, was not so lucky, although because of the Feinberg pack and shark attack treatment procedures, he too survived. A shark stripped the flesh from the bone above his right ankle and tore his foot from the leg, as with the first victim, Cornelius Pyper. His leg had to be amputated below the knee. Jones had been board surfing with two friends about 50 metres from shore when something bumped his toes; he thought he had touched a log. Then, he said, "I felt a clamp and weight on my right ankle." He thought it was one of his friends pulling his leg. Jones lifted his leg and said, "I couldn't believe my eyes when I saw a shark's head clinging to it. It suddenly began to thrash and pulled me partly into the water." Jones pulled his leg upright and "it felt as if I had pulled my foot off. I slid back onto my board and sat and lifted my leg to see if what I felt was true. When I saw the ruin of my leg I just wanted to cry. I couldn't believe it."

Jones reached the beach and a friend helped him up the sand. They used his surfboard leash as a tourniquet until the lifesavers arrived with the shark attack pack. There is no doubt that without the training and knowledge of the lifesavers with the Feinberg shark attack pack that instead of two lower leg amputations, one or more of those attacks would have been fatal. The five Amanzimtoti attacks in 1974–75 showed several factors in common. Four took place in the afternoon and all were in water between one and two metres deep. Four were 50 metres from shore, the fifth was only 3 metres. In all five cases, the sea was discoloured from river water, and all five attacks were in the channel.

The most striking feature of the Natal attacks is the flare-up on the South Coast of three periods of remarkable activity in 1940–43, 1957–61 and 1974–75, with long intervening periods of comparative quiescence.

In the fourteen years between 1943 and 1957, the sharks shifted their attention to Durban and the Umgeni River region.

During the period 1943-51, 21 attacks took place here whilst only 5 were recorded along the whole length of the south coast. With the introduction of meshing at Durban in 1952, apart from the attack on Graham Scott at the Durban rocket hut on 4 January 1954, attacks ceased, not only at Durban, but also along the southern Natal coast. Then on 18 December 1957 there was an attack on Robin Wherley at Karridene, which was followed up just two days later with a fatal attack on Alan Green at Uvongo, further south. These two attacks were the start of a sequence of 26 attacks, 10 of which were fatal, up until 23 February 1975.

It is a reasonable supposition that these outbursts of activity were in some way associated with alterations in sea surface temperatures and that the key lay in the suggestion of Professor J. B. L. Smith, Ichthyologist of Rhodes University, that they were associated with heavy rains in Natal combined with changes in the strong-flowing warm Mozambique current.

Numerous rivers debouch into the sea every 5 or 10 kilometres along the coast of Natal, and another feature which the South African attacks appear to have in common with the Australian is that they have frequently taken place near the mouths of rivers after heavy inland rains and often in murky water.

The South African statistics also support the theory that attacks in the seasonal zones are more common on east than on west coasts. During the period in which more than 40 attacks took place in this zone on the east coast, only 3 were recorded in the west; 1 at Cape Town and 2 in False Bay in the south-western corner.

South African sharks have not confined their attentions to swimmers. In 1946 in Table Bay, a small boat was sunk by a shark, but luckily the occupants were rescued from the circling shark by another boat. Four small boats were attacked in this bay in 1946. False Bay south of Cape Town has been the scene of several boat attacks by white sharks. In 1942 there were two by a reportedly 6.5 metre shark. In 1948 a boat was almost sunk by a shark which, after circling repeatedly, charged the boat and finally holed it. In 1958 at Plattenberg Bay, a white shark grabbed the propeller of a boat while it was trolling. In 1960 in Saldanha Bay, a white shark charged a boat, biting at the transom and breaking teeth on the wood. The boat nearly capsized, and was filling with water when another boat came to its rescue. In October 1960, again in False Bay, a white shark, identified from its tooth fragments, bit a hole in a boat just above the water line. Six boats were damaged in 1970 by white sharks and their close relative the mako.

One of the luckiest survivals and most frightening attacks was in 1977, when a 6 metre twin outboard boat with four fishermen aboard suddenly had a fifth occupant, a big white shark. Before it could be killed, one of the men was seriously hurt. He was taken by a rescue craft to hospital with a crushed pelvis and ruptured bladder. The shark, with jaws still ripping the gunwale, was removed from inside the boat after the boat was towed to port.

In 1974 Danie Schoeman had his boat attacked on three separate occasions in False Bay. In each case, damage was caused to the boat and twice this fisherman returned to port with his attacking white shark. In all, Schoeman has had his boat crashed five times. In all cases, even the one in which the boat was trolling, the shark crashed the boat as fish were being caught. This is in line with South Australian experiences. Great care must be taken by fishermen when large sharks are seen biting and chasing hooked fish and circling boats.

The use of wetsuits and the popularity of surfboard riding has, as in Australia, New Zealand and West Coast US waters, increased the chance of humans and white sharks coming into contact. The South African coast, from the numbers of white sharks caught by fishermen and the size of the sharks, is potentially one of the world's best white shark fisheries. In recent years there have been several typical white shark attacks on South African surfers.

An unusual white shark attack occurred at Buffalo Bay in Cape Province on 11 April 1971, when Theo Klein was fatally attacked. In this attack, instead of the often occurring one bite and retreat by the shark, Klein was attacked repeatedly for twenty minutes in view of several hundred people. Klein was body surfing with his son-in-law when he was suddenly isolated from other bathers. He saw the shark when it was homing in from only a few metres away. The 3 metre white shark bit, and tore into his stomach. After the first massive bite, Klein swam three strokes and then lay face down in the water. The shark kept itself between the body and a rescue attempt on a surfboard, returning repeatedly to tear pieces from Klein's body until the dead man was eventually picked up by a rescue boat.

Surfboard rider David Robertson was more fortunate; he survived an attack by a white shark at Cape St Francis. Robertson rolled off his board and swam to safety while the shark continued to attack the board. The surfboard was washed to the beach fifteen minutes after the attack and had a big piece bitten out of it.

Three other attacks have been recorded for this area, including the first attack documented in South African waters when on 28 January 1886, a man was fatally mauled. The next attack was in the Zwart Kops River at Port Elizabeth, when a Miss T. Toft was bitten on the side of the body. A man named Rodwell was killed at Port Elizabeth in 1930, and then there were no further attacks in the area until the Cape St Francis/Seal Point attacks on David Robertson and visiting Australian surfboard rider Marshall Flanagan.

Flanagan and a friend, Andrew Mair, were surfing off Seal Point on 6 October 1976. Flanagan had paddled out to seek another wave when Mair saw a fin making towards Flanagan. He yelled "Shark" just as a white shark struck and bit hard into Flanagan's left thigh with its upper teeth and into the board with its lower. Flanagan hit the shark on the head several times and damaged his hand when the shark's teeth cut tendons in two fingers. The shark did not return to the attack and Flanagan reached shore with a large flap of skin and muscle hanging from his thigh. A tooth fragment found in this injury identified the attacker as a white shark. This incident is similar to those involving board surfers off the California and Oregon coasts.

A South African lifesaver was twice bitten while body surfing and survived. He was first bitten by a shark on 26 March 1944, and almost four years later, on 8 March 1947, he was again bitten only 400 metres from where he was first attacked. On both occasions he was only bitten once and not molested again while returning to shore.

The Oceanographic Research Institute at Durban has made a special study of first-aid management of the victims of shark attacks and methods, which can result in the recovery of victims as severely injured as Michael Hely, deserve more than passing mention. Those concerned say that their success in this and other cases is due to efficient beach resuscitation and to the use of the newer and more powerful antibiotics.

Their motto is **treat them on the beach**. Allow thirty minutes or even an hour for the victims' anti-stress mechanisms to come into play before rushing them to hospital. Rush the transfusion to the patient rather than the patient to the transfusion. Their advice is "Keep the patient still, cold and in the head-down position. Rely on the power of the newer antibiotics. These have reduced the need for radical and emergency surgery." It is believed that rushing a seriously injured victim prematurely from the scene of an accident or shark attack is much more likely to end in death.

The main points in the South African method of shark attack treatment are (a) Blood should be rushed to the patient, not the patient to the blood. This helps ease the effect of shock. Prior preparations should be made in likely attack areas. The Feinberg Pack of South Africa has proved most effective. (b) The patient should be kept lying head down above the wave line. (c) Telephone for ambulance and doctor, advising need of blood. (d) Apply tourniquets at once. Control bleeding with cloths or bandages. Lay people should do no more than this. (e) Do not administer alcohol or hot drinks, simply cover the patient with a towel or light cover. Sips of fresh water may be given. (f) Antibiotics will cut the chances of infection, so the wounds can be cleaned later. (g) Remember that shock can be as big a killer as the shark. So reduce panic and confusion.

The Feinberg Pack consists of swabs, spirits, tourniquets; one Vaco Liter of normal saline; one bottle of dried human plasma; two plastic intravenous giving sets; ampoules of morphine, coramine and noradrenaline; a syringe. This pack can be kept in doctors' rooms or ambulance stations. In South Africa the packs are placed at thirty places along the 160 kilometres of shark-infested coastline.

SHARKS IN THE PACIFIC

Among the innumerable islands of the Pacific the shark to the natives is part of life, death and eternity. To hundreds of thousands of Pacific Islanders it is a romantic and awesome figure which holds an extraordinary place in their esteem.

Sharks' teeth are widely used for charms, amulets, surgical instruments and weapons, and the status of a man among his fellows is often determined, not so much by his prowess in war, as by his dexterity and daring in shark combat. The shark figures abundantly in the mythology and legend of these people, and shark gods and demigods provide the basis of many of their cults and religions. In Hawaii and other places sharks have been appeased with human sacrifices. The culture of the South Seas is rich in shark lore. The Fijian natives have legends of Dakuwaga, a mythical 12 metre shark which lifted whole boats from the water, and the Polynesians have built up a fascinating mythology, in which sharks, shark gods and beings combining the features of sharks and humans play prominent parts.

In the Solomons sharks are worshipped. The natives of the Torres Strait erect shrines to hammerhead sharks and there are similar cults in the Carolines. The Maoris of New Zealand at one time revered the mako shark which they called Ngutikao and caught with a noose. Maoris who had teeth from a mako and wore them suspended from holes bored in the ear lobes, were of great rank and importance.

The most famous legend in the oral literature of the South Seas is the Maui myth, or Maui cycle, which extends throughout the Pacific islands. This classic, the "Homeric Odyssey of the Pacific", is best known in Polynesia but is also widespread in Micronesia and Melanesia. It is a household word in Hawaii, New Zealand, the New Hebrides and Yap. Captain Cook was the first European to discover the legend. Maui was half god, half man. One of the stories refers to a shark, Mokoroa, which insulted Maui while he was fishing up islands. Maui killed Mokoroa with his spear and with a mighty heave threw him high into the sky where, according to the Maoris, the Pukapukans and the Raratongans, he can still be seen lying upon the Milky Way. According to the Maui legend, Tahiti is one of Maui's sharks which escaped to its present location.

The early missionaries also wrote of the Polynesian's dread of sharks. As these people voyaged among the islands it was the shark alone that presented danger. While certain types of shark were killed and eaten by them, the blue shark and others were deified.

Rather than attempt to destroy them, they tried to propitiate them by prayers and offerings. The fishermen, who went most to sea, naturally prayed louder and longer than anyone else. Even temples, with officiating priests, were erected to these marine horrors. The natives believed the sharks recognised the priests and would not injure them.

It is said the Auki islanders would never kill a shark. They believed a shark would never attack them and were reported to bathe quite happily in the sea when sharks could be seen swimming about in the water. Some years ago Lieutenant Vaughan-Jones, RN, described a remarkable ceremony carried out by these islanders with two large sharks they regarded as sacred and treated more or less as pets. The natives of another island, Lifou, also have no fear of the sharks which abound in its fertile waters. They believe their ancestors made a non-aggression pact with the monsters and that it has always been respected by both parties. But mindful of the unhappy fate of many other non-aggression pacts, the natives, to make sure they won't be attacked, swim about making a lot of noise and with a piece of *manou* trailing behind them. They also cover the lighter coloured bottoms of their feet with black sandals, for the few times the natives have been attacked was because the bottoms of their feet were apparently mistaken by the sharks for the light-bellied sandfish.

These people at times chase small sharks 1.5 to 2 metres long and asphyxiate them by lifting them from the water. They never attack any of the shark family with a weapon as they say the shedding of blood would break the non-aggression pact.

The islanders have so much trust in this agreement that they allow their young children to fish all day up to 3 kilometres from the shore. The children float with the help of a dried coconut under each arm, bobbing up and down in the water while they fish with their handlines. They are never disturbed by sharks.

One of the most popular misconceptions about sharks is that dark-skinned swimmers have charmed lives, and sharks do not attack them. It probably arises from the fact that in the common practice of throwing coins from ocean liners few of the natives diving for them are attacked. The blood of many a person, however, has proved the belief is a misconception. There have been reports of dark-skinned divers being taken by sharks in the harbours of Aden, Singapore, Port Moresby, Colombo and Suva. Indeed it is possible that if all the facts were known it would be found that the dark-skinned swimmers attacked by sharks would far outnumber the white.

News from all the Pacific Islands is largely by word of mouth and it is likely that only a fraction of the number of attacks which occur are recorded. Reports of attacks on bathers, divers, fishermen and underwater swimmers in the central Pacific have come from Papua, Guadalcanal, the Solomons, New Caledonia, New Hebrides, Wake Island, Fiji, Pago Pago, Tahiti and Hawaii.

Many of these people have exhibited almost superhuman powers of endurance. Shark attacks on Pacific Islanders seem to bring this quality to the surface. Some years ago a native was attacked by a big shark at Singour, 100 kilometres from Madang, on the north coast of New Guinea. He was swimming with others when he was attacked from behind. Shouts and screams from the others scared the brute off. The victim was carried ashore. He had a huge wound extending from the small of the back to his thigh. He was taken in a canoe on a trip to Saidor outpost, 50 kilometres away. A plane with a twelve-hour medical orderly flew to Saidor and took him to Madang Hospital. There he made satisfactory progress.

The story of Sindilin, a native of Lou Island, off Manus, in the Admiralty group (lat. 2°22′S) is also typical of the en-

A shark which attacked schoolchildren at Madang Guinea.
(PHOTOGRAH BY *MR S. DICZBALIS*)

durance and courage of these islanders. Mr Lloyd Tonkin, in a letter to Pastor R. E. Hare of Wahroonga, New South Wales, told the following story:

> Mrs Tonkin and I were stationed on Lou Island at the time and it was about midday when Nokas arrived from the other side of the island to inform us what had happened. When we saw Sindilin his right arm was lacerated to shreds somewhat below the elbow, and the bones (radius and ulna) were smashed to pieces. The blood vessels were severed and the hand simply hung to what flesh and skin was left. The left arm and hand were also lacerated badly but not to the same extent.
>
> The restrictive bandages (improvised from the rubber on his speargun) Nokas had applied were the salvation of Sindilin's life. He could not have lasted any time if it had not been for the resourcefulness of Nokas, who applied his knowledge of first aid in a very brave and skilful manner. It would have been folly for Mrs Tonkin and I to alter what he had done. It was obvious all the essential work had been done and what was left (namely amputation) could only be done by a doctor. Apart from a little cleaning up we did nothing. Sindilin was then taken by canoe on at least a 10-hour trip to Lombrum where he received the attention of the doctor (it was a nasty ocean, too).

Nokas's own story is one of those little-known epics of unsung heroes that come on rare occasions. Nokas wrote:

> During the month of May 1955, ten boys from the mission school of Pisik and I went to fishing along the coast where the reef was half a mile [about a kilometre] away from the shore. As we went along nine of us went diving together. One boy, Sindilin, came with me and dived in search of fish. Sindilin was diving well out beyond the reef while I was just on the edge of the reef.
>
> As Sindilin came up to the surface I saw a shark strike. It took Sindilin just below the elbow on the right arm and tore the flesh from the forearm leaving the bones bare and the hand badly lacerated. I had my spear gun loaded and immediately swam to where Sindilin was struggling with the

shark. I unloaded my spear gun at the shark but it missed.
Again the shark came towards us. I grabbed Sindilin and
started to swim with him to where the water was shallow.

The shark struck again and lacerated Sindilin's left forearm
while we were just on the edge of the reef. When we got to the
shallow water I immediately removed the rubber thongs of my
gun and applied a tourniquet above the elbow on his right
arm.

Then I succeeded in getting Sindilin into the shore. Between
the reef and the shore was half a mile [about a kilometre] of
deep water, but without stopping I pushed Sindilin into the
water and swam with him. When we got to the shore Sindilin
was only semi-conscious. He spoke to me and said "Nokas, I
think I am going to die," but I said nothing to him. I shouted
for the other boys with the canoe. When they arrived we put
Sindilin in it and I asked the boys to row the canoe home.
One boy and I kept Sindilin comfortable on the canoe.

When we came to the shore where a path goes through the
village of Kon I asked the other boys to stay with Sindilin and
I ran to the village to let Mr Tonkin know before the arrival
of the canoe and prepare things we needed to help Sindilin in
order to save his life. Up the hills and vales I ran about three
miles [5 kilometres] from the canoe to the village of Kon. I
told everybody to get ready for the arrival of the canoe with
Sindilin, and to push a big canoe into the water to take
Sindilin across the big ocean between the island of Lou and
big Manus.

That was about 20 miles [about 30 kilometres] distant.
When we reached to the doctor he looked over Sindilin's body
and asked, "Who did this?" I answered, "I did, sir."

"Who instructed you to do this?"

I said, "Nobody instructed me, but our Mission showed us
how to save life."

The doctor said nothing further to me but went on with his
work.

There are some weird tales told about Pacific divers' battles
with sharks. In the Dangerous Islands (the Tuamotus) a bad-
tempered local diver came face to face with an equally bad-
tempered 3.5 metre shark. This shark, like practically every other

in existence, did not differentiate between the colour of divers' skins. The diver was quietly gathering pearlshell when he bumped into the great creature. The shark circled and slid into the attack. The diver took refuge in a coral cavern, but the shark came in right behind him. Seeing no other means of escape, the diver struggled desperately onto the shark's back and buried his fingers deeply into its gill slits.

This was an unexpected turn of events for the shark. It became terrified and rushed to the surface with such speed that it shot clear of the water, turned in mid-air, dived to the bottom again and then resurfaced with the diver hanging on like a bronco buster. Maddened, the shark headed towards a slightly submerged reef where it beached, high and dry. The diver slid from the monster's back and walked unaided to the beach, his body torn and bloody from the shark's rough skin and collisions with the sharp coral. He thought the matter over for a few minutes, worked himself into a rage, strode back to the shark and aimed a terrific blow at its snout with his fist. The shark's mouth flashed open and took off his hand.

No story of sharks in the Pacific would be complete without recounting the tremendous part they have played in the lives of Hawaiians. To them sharks were gods of fear. Hawaiian history is full of this strange lore.

Shark gods and goddesses were many, and as divinities the shark gods were in a class with the fearful Pele, the goddess of the volcano. Hawaiian folklore abounds with deified sharks who, the natives said, had supernatural powers and could assume human shape at will. Each of the Hawaiian islands had its shark kings and queens, and off Honolulu Harbour lived the greatest of them all, the king and ruler of all sharks with great powers of magic — Kamo-hoa-lii. The home of Oahu, the queen of the sharks, was at the bottom of Pearl Harbor and she decreed the waters of Oahu tabu for all man-eaters.

Otto von Kotzebue, who in the 1820s went on a voyage of discovery in the South Seas and Bering Strait, reported that in the Pearl River there were sharks of remarkable size and there had been many instances of them swallowing people alive. On the banks the natives had made an artificial pond of coral stones. In it was a large shark. Von Kotzebue was told the people threw adults, but more often children, into the pool.

The shark pen at Pearl Harbor is often referred to in early Hawaiian literature. It was a ring of rocks enclosing about 1.5 hectares of water, with an opening on the seaward side. The sharks were enticed into the pool by food. Then the opening was closed. Gladiatorial contests with the sharks were held, accompanied by much celebration and feasting. The only weapon the gladiator used was a long stick armed with a shark's tooth.

Two Hawaiian sayings suggest the natives noticed the seasonal variations of shark attacks and that they are more likely to occur when the water is warm. "The shark will bite," goes one saying, "when the wili wili tree is in bloom." There is another: "Take care, the sea is warm, a shark is close by."

Not one of the Hawaiian race rose to shatter the faith of the people in deified sharks until the mighty Queen Kapiolani defied Pele's alleged power. Then shark worship, shark sacrifice and the tender rearing of young sharks for protective influence passed.

In Hawaii it is said very few people have been attacked by sharks while swimming as the instances of shark bite, including eleven fatalities, since 1880 have been primarily cases of fishermen. The comparative safety of Hawaiian waters was attributed to the activity of the Japanese fishermen of the islands, who waged an annual campaign against sharks. They netted 2700 kilograms daily for the Honolulu market. This left fewer sharks to cause trouble.

Hawaii was particularly disturbed by an attack which took place near Twin Islands (Mokolua Island) about a kilometre off Lanikai on 13 December 1958. The victim, 15-year-old Billy Weaver, was one of a party of six boys swimming and surfing near a reef. They had with them three coloured surfboards and a 2.5 metre sailing boat. At 1 p.m., while two of the boys were resting on the boat, the other four were surfing off the reef with air mattresses and a surfboard. All but Billy Weaver, on an air mattress, caught the wave. After they had gone about 50 metres they heard him crying out. When they swam over to him they found him in a pool of blood with a leg missing. He then disappeared. His body was located later by a helicopter crew and recovered.

The shark, which is believed to have been a tiger shark about 3.5 to 4.5 metres long, continued to cruise in the area, but was not captured. Suggestions were made at the time that the coloured air mattresses, fish traps or a sea turtle, which was found nearby, had attracted the shark inside the reef.

The attack caused immediate and widespread concern and a public demand for action. Bounties were offered for all large sharks caught in the area. An action programme for reducing the shark abundance by the adoption of a scientifically directed shark fishing scheme was proposed. On 1 April 1959, the Billy Weaver Shark Control Programme was started and purchased a vessel by public subscription. Using 24-hook long line gear 595 sharks were caught in inshore waters during the remainder of the year. Of these, 71 were tiger sharks.

Hawaii's magnificent oceanarium, Sea Life Park, near Honolulu, is using part of its gate receipts for research into marine life as well as providing informative enjoyment to countless people every year in the most beautiful setting possible. Pelagic sharks of various species can be observed at different water levels in a transplanted living coral reef.

Farther east there have been a number of attacks along the Californian coast. But from the tropical shores of Central America, Ecuador and Peru reports have been few and documented evidence scant. There was a report of a young girl being killed on the beach at Manzanilla in Mexico. Several attacks have also been reported in the Gulf of Panama. Other accounts tell of tuna fishermen being dragged out of fishing boats by their catch amongst great shoals of fish, and then being attacked by sharks. It is doubtful if any attacks take place farther south along the coast of Chile.

In the north-western Pacific, attacks are believed to be common, but little information has been available beyond odd reports of attacks in China, Hong Kong and the Philippines. Elsewhere throughout Asia and South-East Asia, little or no information has generally been available.

More detailed and definite information has, however, been received from Singapore. From time to time attacks there have been reported on Japanese "listeners". These are men specially trained to listen underwater for shoals of fish which they detect by a rustling noise. At times they are too intent on listening for fish to notice the sharks.

Attacks at Singapore are few. About 1926 a woman visiting Singapore, diving from a stage anchored some distance from the beach at Sea View Swimming Club, literally dived into a shark's mouth. When she came to the surface she was being violently shaken in the shark's jaws. She was immediately pulled onto the diving stage. A young doctor, Dr Arthur Dickson Wright — later a well-known London surgeon — rushed down with his kit of surgical instruments. He found the unfortunate woman bleeding profusely from a torn femoral artery. Dr Wright tied the artery, but it was too late. The woman died from the effects of shock and haemorrhage. A few days before a Chinese fisherman had been bitten within several hundred metres of this fatal spot.

The most widely known attack in the area was on an old Malay diver named Abdullah. Abdullah used to dive for pennies in Singapore Harbour. One of his favourite tricks was to dive with a lighted cigar in his mouth and come up still smoking it. He dived for many years without any trouble, but about 1950 his luck turned. He was killed by a shark.

In July 1954, a Royal Navy frogman was fatally attacked in Singapore Harbour. He was attacked 6 metres below the surface, when the visibility underwater was only 60 centimetres. Another frogman was down about 30 metres away and surfaced unaware of the attack. The attack was evidently made from the right side and rear of the frogman and was mainly directed to his right thigh. He was wearing only bathing trunks and his oxygen apparatus was painted black. He managed to struggle to the surface 100 metres from shore.

A rescue party reached the site of the blood on the water and an officer went to the man's aid. Customs and naval officers pulled him from the water, but he died soon after. There is no positive evidence that a shark was responsible for this attack, but the wide crescentic shape of the wound appeared to be consistent with a shark bite.

There have never been any other shark reports in this particular part of the harbour. The area, however, is densely packed with local shipping, from which refuse is being continually dumped.

The International Shark Attack file listed the attack as No. 367 and has the information that water visibility was less than a metre. Yet another instance of turbid water and low visibility giving a high risk of shark attack.

SHARK ATTACKS
IN THE UNITED STATES

All the coastal states of the United States lie within the world shark attack belt although for years people in the United States were reluctant to believe that shark attacks occurred on their shores, but a search through newspaper and other files shows that attacks on bathers and underwater swimmers by sharks, barracuda or some other sea creatures are much more common than is generally supposed.

Recent claims have been made that sharks in the United States are becoming a serious menace. Whilst this is undoubtedly an exaggeration, there is little doubt that their number is increasing. Over 200 attacks have been recorded in United States waters, with 31 known fatalities.

Attacks have been reported from the following 13 states: Connecticut, Delaware, Massachusetts, Mississippi, New York, New Jersey, North Carolina, South Carolina, Georgia, Florida, Texas, California and Oregon.

The pattern of attacks in the United States has much in common with the Australian attacks. But when mortality rates are considered it is evident that the sharks in the United States have not the same killer instinct as their counterparts in Australia.

The attacks fall into several groups. Those in the New York area form one group and the savage attacks by the "mad shark" of New Jersey in 1916 another. The attacks which took place in the Charleston area of South Carolina form a strange and unusual group. Attacks on the Florida coast have other features. On the west coast, too, there appear to be differences between the attacks at San Francisco, Monterey Bay and Los Angeles.

On the east coast the most northerly attack took place at Hollywood Beach, just above Mattapoisett Harbour, Buzzard's Bay, Massachusetts, a little after 3 p.m. on 25 July 1936. Sixteen-year-old Joseph Troy, Jr, of Dorchester, was swimming about 150 metres off the shore in water about 4 metres deep. He was with an older man, Walter W. Stiles, of Boston. They were about 3 metres apart. Stiles was swimming quietly, but Troy, using a "crawl" stroke, was making considerable commotion in the water.

Without warning, a shark appeared at Troy's left side (the side away from Stiles) and grabbed the lad's left leg. Troy was dragged underwater before he could utter a sound. The momentum carried both the shark and the lad closer to Stiles, who recognised the attacker as a shark. With great courage he trod the water while Troy fought the shark and came to the surface. He swam to his friend, caught him with one hand and paddled with the other. All the while he shouted for help.

The shouts were heard by Mr and Mrs Herbert Fisher, of Dorchester Centre, Massachusetts. Mr Fisher jumped into a dory and rowed to where Stiles was supporting the wounded boy. Fisher and Stiles, with difficulty, got Troy into the boat, then the exhausted Stiles was helped aboard. The shark stood off in the blood-reddened water only a few metres away, seemingly ready to make another attack. Troy died five hours later at St Luke's Hospital, New Bedford.

A shark undoubtedly made the attack. It was believed to be the great white shark. Dr Smith, an authority, who identified it, compiled a list of twenty definite records of *Carcharodon* in and near Buzzard's Bay from 1871 to 1927, and at the end he notes: "This list is by no means complete."

This was not the only shark scare in these waters during the summer of 1936. Three days after the attack on Troy, several fishermen in a small boat caught a shark which snapped their lines. It chased the boat and nearly capsized it. About fourteen days later a large shark chased a swimmer, John Donohoe, off Connecticut Point, but it was driven off by two friends threshing the water with a shovel and a bag of clams.

The only other shark incident which had previously been reported from this area took place on 20 August 1916, when a shark "disturbed" some swimmers in a long-distance race between Race Point, Provincetown and Nantucket Beach, but no one was injured.

Farther south a few other incidents have been reported near

New York. In July 1920 Thomas McCann, aged 30, an expert swimmer, disappeared in Woodcliff Channel, Freeport, Long Island, and it was thought he had been taken by a shark, but this was never definitely proved. In 1931 a soldier was also said to have been bitten by a shark or large fish while swimming on the ocean side of Sandy Hook, but again this lacks any supporting evidence. The only other shark reports from this area are of fishermen's injuries and minor injuries to swimmers.

Few attacks, however, can equal for ferocity the remarkable series of attacks farther south, described elsewhere, which took place off the coast of New Jersey in July 1916.

After this, swimmers enjoyed freedom from attack in New Jersey waters for many years. There were, however, several incidents. In 1923, a shark being hoisted aboard a fishing boat off Ocean City broke a man's leg with a flick of its tail. In 1926, a boy's body was found in the sea off Sea Bright. He had apparently been killed by a shark. In 1935 a fisherman sustained serious injuries 80 kilometres off Wildwood, when a shark jumped into his boat.

On 21 August 1960, the truce between sharks and swimmers ended. John Brodeur, aged 24, standing waist-deep in water at Sea Girt, was attacked about 20 metres from the shore. He recovered, but his leg had to be amputated. A curious co-incidence was that the attack took place at almost the same spot where Charles Bruder had been fatally attacked in 1916.

Next day, at Seaside Park several kilometres away, a 14-year-old boy, Thomas McDonald, claimed that a shark had bitten him on the knee. His injuries were not serious. His doctor said he believed the boy must have barked his shin on a piece of driftwood as he dived through the waves.

This second incident caused general alarm. Beach after beach was closed. At other beaches, bathers were restricted to the water's edge. The United States Navy, the New York Police and the Coastguard came into the picture. The Navy sent up a crew of twenty men in a blimp on a shark alert, while the police sent out boats manned by officers armed with rifles and tommy-guns and with a cover of two radio-equipped helicopters as scouts. The Coastguard provided riflemen in rowing boats.

After several fruitless days, the patrols were discontinued for lack of sharks. The *New York Herald Tribune* commented that the only recorded haul from a whole day's adventures off Coney Island was "a small herring caught by a medium-sized boy".

Eight days later, at Ocean City, about 100 kilometres south, a shark attacked a 24-year-old Korean medical student, causing severe lacerations to his leg and exposing the muscles of his thigh. He was swimming half a kilometre from the shore. Lifeguards rescued him in a boat.

Sharks were reported to be more numerous than usual along the New Jersey coast. Scares continued until well into September. In one day off Sandy Hook, tuna fishermen caught eleven blue sharks over 2.5 metres long and an even larger white shark.

Along the coast of South Carolina, especially in the Charleston area, attacks have occurred with unusual features. They differed in several ways from most other shark attacks. The wounds, although at times extensive, generally were less severe than in shark attacks in most other parts of the world. The mortality was nil and in eleven attacks all the victims recovered.

These attacks were the subject of an investigation by E. Milby Burton, the Director of the Charleston Museum, in 1935. Burton reported them as far back as July 1907, when a man received slight injuries to his leg in a small creek near Coles Island. On 29 May 1919, W. E. Davis was attacked in James Island Sound. Describing the event, Mr Davis said:

> *It must have been a vicious fish and an intentional attack because I had no warning whatsoever. Further, the water that afternoon was exceptionally clear so that the shark could not have been mistaken as to what it was attacking. Also, I was swimming vigorously and making quite a commotion in the water. Under those conditions I think it was a hungry, vicious shark that intentionally attacked me and had I been farther out in the Sound would have attacked me again.*

In 1924 and 1925 two further attacks took place. On 31 July 1924, Lewis Kornahrens received injuries to his left leg and knee at Folly Island. A year later almost to the day Mrs Walter H. Kahrs sustained lacerations to her body, thigh and hip, also at Folly Island.

Various opinions were expressed concerning the attacker. The

TOP: *Portion of a tooth of the Charleston shark (USA) removed from wounds of Lewis Kornahrens, who was attacked by a shark on Folly Island, Charleston County, South Carolina, 31 July 1924 (Museum Spec. 2811). Identified as the tooth of a young mackerel (mako) shark.*

RIGHT: *Mako shark, Cronulla.*

LEFT: *Head and teeth of a mako shark which attacked a boat at Cronulla.*

attack on Lewis Kornahrens provided an important clue. After he was discharged from hospital, his knee cap swelled. He was readmitted to hospital, another operation was performed and a fragment of tooth still in the possession of the Charleston Museum was removed.

The fragment was sent to the American Museum of Natural History in New York, where it was examined by Doctors Gudger and Nichols. They reported there was no doubt the tooth was a shark's and not a barracuda's, as some people had suggested. Probably, the doctors said, the tooth came from a young mackerel shark.

In 1933 three more attacks took place within two months, two of them within a week of each other. Emma Megginson received injuries to her left leg at Folly Island on 16 June 1933. Five days later at the north end of Morris Island at the mouth of Charleston Harbour, 15-year-old Dayton Hastie received injuries to his knee.

Dayton Hastie, describing the attack, said:

Far up the shore line, I saw what I thought might be the dorsal fin of a large shark cutting the rough surface. I stood up and strained my eyes to make certain. I concluded it must be a fin. Reaching the place and finding nothing that resembled a fin, I believed I had mistaken a choppy wave for one.

I didn't like the idea of swimming with sharks all around, so I sat down in about three feet [a metre] of water. There the beach sloped gradually until about six feet [2 metres] beyond where I was sitting, it made a deep drop. I was almost certain that in such shallow water, I would be safe enough from anything large enough to bite.

I felt a swerve of water which was immediately followed by an impact. Something clamped down on my right leg. I was being pulled outward by something which seemed to have the power of a horse.

Looking down I saw amid the foam and splashing, the head of a large shark with my knee in its mouth, shaking it as a puppy would shake a stick while trying to take it from someone. I started kicking frantically with my unharmed leg to free myself. I freed my right leg. Then the monster bit me on the left. All this time I had been pulling myself up on the

*beach backwards with my hands and kicking at the rough
head of the shark. It seemed to be as solid as Gibraltar. All
this happened in about 10 seconds.*

*Although some people said I had been bitten by everything
from crabs to whales, I still have a perfect design of a shark's
mouth around my knee measuring 10 inches [25 centimetres]
across. This confirms the statement of my friend who was
standing on the bank. He said the shark was easily 8 feet [2.5
metres] long.*

The week before and the week after the last attack, two
2.5 metre sharks were taken within 100 metres of the site of
the incident. They were identified as yellow or cub sharks
(*Hypoprion brevirostris*), believed to be natives of the West
Indies rather than the Atlantic coast. No shark of this species
had been recorded in the area from 1882 to 1932, when a small
specimen was caught by the Charleston Museum staff. Two
months after the attack on Dayton Hastie, Kenneth Layton was
attacked at Pawley's Island 120 kilometres north of Charleston.

In July 1941 a soldier stationed at Port Moultrie, on Sullivan's
Island at the mouth of Charleston Harbour, was mauled.
There followed an interval of fifteen years without any attacks.
Then, in July 1956, Eric Rawle, aged 7, was attacked while
swimming in very shallow water on the Island of Palms,
Charleston County. In the reports of this attack it was stated
the shape of the wounds left little doubt his attacker was a
shark. On 16 July 1968, P. M. Hughes was spearfishing at
Stono Inlet near Charleston with five others when a shark
estimated at 4 metres in length ignored the fish that had been
speared and bit Hughes's flipper. It then chased another diver
before returning to Hughes and biting him on the knee. A
rescuer in a boat stabbed the shark in the back when it returned
to attack Hughes as he was being hauled inboard.

The only other incident reported from South Carolina was
when Ted Roach was violently bumped by a shark as he was
floating on his back in the Oketee River in July 1949.

No review of shark attacks and incidents along the eastern
coast of the United States would be complete without the story
of W. J. Pierpont, Jr, of Georgia, whose life was saved by his
wife's presence of mind.

On 3 June 1917, at Calibogue Sound, Pierpont, his wife and

children were spending the day on his launch. He stopped the vessel in shallow water, intending to take the children for a swim. Grabbing the painter he jumped overboard. The water was deeper than he thought, and the next instant he was struggling below the surface. Then the horror-stricken wife saw a shark appear directly above the spot where her husband had gone under. Pierpont surfaced alongside the shark. The man seemed to have no chance. In sight of his wife and children the shark snapped its great jaws. One of the shouting, struggling man's arms was almost severed at the shoulder.

Pierpont and his threshing attacker shot below the surface together. All the screaming wife and children could see was bloodstained water. Mrs Pierpont pulled on the painter with all her strength. Pierpont still held it and he came slowly to the surface. The woman dragged her husband into the launch. His right arm was in shreds and dangled from the shoulder.

They were 30 kilometres from Savannah and help. Mrs Pierpont ripped her skirt and bandaged the terrible wounds as best she could. With her husband lying helpless in the launch's bottom, the wife started the motor and sped off on the long journey. Fifteen kilometres out she sighted a pilot boat. The vessel put a crew member on board the launch. While Mrs Pierpont comforted her husband the man raced the launch to Savannah. Here Pierpont was taken to hospital. The arm was operated on and he recovered.

One difference between attacks in the United States and Australia is that when a person is attacked in Australia and most other waters there is no argument that the attack was made by a shark. But in the United States the barracuda is sometimes blamed for the attacks. The barracuda bites shear in a straight line, whereas sharks leave a circular imprint from their wide tearing and holding jaws.

Sometimes known as the "tiger fish" or "long-nosed sea pike" on account of the length of its snout, the barracuda has two rows of pointed razor-sharp teeth in its upper jaw and one row in the lower. It is not as big as a shark and hasn't the jaw mechanism capable of rending a limb in one bite.

Shipwreck survivors have at times complained that barracuda stalked lifeboats and rafts and bit their legs in the water. Hans Hass states dogmatically there can be no doubt that barracuda occasionally attack and kill human beings. In Brazil, the barracuda is dreaded more than the shark and in the Caribbean, where it is commonly found, it is also regarded as a dangerous fish, particularly savage when caught in a net. Reports by skindivers, however, suggest that the ferocity of this fish has been overestimated and that it has at times been confused with the shark.

Florida attacks, some fatal on swimmers, and skindivers are of various types. The myth about the presence of dolphins or porpoises indicating that sharks are not in the vicinity was again disproved at Panama City, Florida, when on 16 October 1963, William Cheatham was attacked while beach fishing. He was wading and casting only 9 metres from shore. He was bitten severely on his right calf, and was knocked down and shaken by the shark. Cheatham escaped after physically wrestling with the shark while avoiding its mouth, and reached safety on shore while the shark nearly stranded itself in the shallows as it chased him through the clear water. Cheatham clearly remembers seeing schools of porpoises only 90 metres offshore before the attack.

Warm clear water, the reefs and abundant fish population of Florida make it an ideal area for visitors and locals to enjoy all water sports, including underwater activities. As in other areas, spearfishing and the resulting vibration from the speared fish and possible blood and slime in the water have increased the odds of confrontation and attack.

A reef 8 kilometres south of prestigious Palm Beach was the scene for such a confrontation on 22 August 1964. Kenny Ruszenas had just speared a fish in 12 metres of water when a 3.5 metre hammerhead shark homed in on him and opened its mouth wide as it came close. At about three-quarters of a metre distance Ruszenas pushed the tip of his speargun under the shark's head, lifted, and forced the hammerhead to swim over him. Then as he turned he saw the shark coming at him again at chest level. His speargun slid off the shark's flat nose and he had to push the shark away with his hands. Shark and diver were now back near the surface and the shark swam away. Ruszenas had no doubt that the shark was intending to bite as it came at him with its mouth wide open.

Palm Beach was also the scene of an unusual attack on 20

April 1968, when 10-year-old Stephen Samples was swimming with swim fins and mask in water less than 2 metres deep. Stephen saw what he thought may have been a shark turning away just as it struck him. He yelled, "Daddy, sharks, sharks." His father, who was just leaving the water, immediately re-entered and swam towards his son. Suddenly he saw a small shark swimming towards him. So he dived, waved his arms and the shark veered away. As he approached Stephen he saw "an enormous fin of a shark" behind his son, who was beating at the water with his hands. The boy swam towards his father and disappeared briefly below the surface. As father and son met, other rescuers arrived with a surfboard and the boy was brought to shore. Stephen said he felt a "crunching sensation" in his back and buttocks as he was pulled under the water. There were many witnesses to the attack, who saw several sharks during and after the attack. One shark was about 3 metres long, and the others, estimated to number between four to eight, were 1.25 to 2 metres. Teeth fragments from Stephen's wounds were identified as being from a carcharinid, a whaler type, probably the silky shark.

An investigation of the circumstances leading to this aggregation of sharks, and their pugnacity, disclosed that other people had baited and chummed the area ready for a nighttime shark fishing expedition. Stephen did not lose flesh, but his wounds required about 1000 stitches. Another interesting feature of this attack was that the severe wounds in his legs were made on one side only. On the swim fins, the cuts were on the bottom side of each fin, which in swimming action would be on the top side. The attack was one of a series in Florida, which is 1968 resulted in a meeting of a committee to discuss how to reduce the incidence of shark confrontations and attacks.

Dr David Baldridge, in his 1973 paper "Shark attack against Man — a programme of data reduction and analysis", listed 111 attacks in Florida waters.

Included among the fatal cases was a ship's pilot, who in 1911 dived overboard to rescue a drowning man in Pensacola Bay and two swimmers at Key West; one of whom, an Air Force pilot, was wearing a fluorescent bathing suit.

In two other fatal attacks, one on a university student at St Augustine, Florida, on 4 August 1947, and the other on Dorothy MacLatchie at St Petersburg on the west coast of Florida, in

June 1922, barracuda were blamed. In each instance the wounds suggested that they were likely to have been made by a shark.

Besides these fatalities, a Navy pilot lost his life scuba diving in the Gulf of Mexico and a fisherman was killed trying to secure a shark inside a net. In another doubtful attack, the remains of a man were found inside a shark. It was presumed he had been attacked before death, but the evidence for this was scant.

A special feature of the Florida attacks has been that in a number of instances small sharks made the attacks, causing only minor wounds. In three instances the shark clung so firmly to its victim that it had to be forcibly removed. In three other instances, sharks retaliated and bit skindivers who had grabbed them by the tail; even sharks 60 centimetres in length resented this familiarity.

Attacks have also been reported in the islands east of Florida — there was an attack at Bermuda in July 1954, and in August 1948, a French scientist was attacked while goggle-fishing at Bimini in the Bahamas. Besides these attacks other incidents involving boats and fishermen have been reported. On 4 August 1961 a 2 metre black-tipped shark grabbed spearfisherman Robert Sato's right hand. The shark continued to menace Sato and his companion on the surface. It came at Sato and veered only when Sato's companion hit the shark on the nose with the point of his spear. The shark made a tight circle and then came straight in, in a manner described as "hunched and mouth wide open". Sato's companion again hit the shark with his spear point for the shark to turn away and give the spearfishermen time to regain the safety of their boat.

Although the number of recorded instances is too few for definite conclusions, it is interesting to note that along the east coast of the United States, sharks appear to follow a timetable and that if the attacks are tabulated the result resembles the Australian table in reverse. According to the timetable, attacks can be expected on the east coast of the United States as follows:

New York	*June–August*
New Jersey	*June–August*
North Carolina	*June–August*
South Carolina	*May–September*
Northern Florida	*April–October*
Southern Florida	*March–November*

So far every recorded attack except one appears to conform to the timetable. (In California, by contrast, attacks have been recorded year-round.)

The west coast of the United States has also participated in the recent general increase in the number of shark attacks along the United States coast. It was not until the attack on Barry Wilson in Monterey Bay in December 1952, that swimmers in California became shark conscious. Previously, shark news in California had been confined mainly to occasional reports of sharks menacing people on surfboards or causing minor injuries to swimmers near Coronado and San Diego. An attack on a boy and his dog in San Francisco Bay in 1926 had long since been forgotten.

In the period 1926 to 1984, California and Oregon coasts recorded 59 shark attacks. Of these 41 were in the period 1952 to 1984. Of these 59 attacks, white sharks have been responsible for 46, blue sharks have been responsible for 2, and unknown species have been responsible for 9. For the period 1979 to 1984, 12 unprovoked attacks took place off California and Oregon. Seven surfboard riders were attacked including 1 on a long board, 3 skin divers, 1 scuba diver and 1 swimmer. Two of the attacks were fatal. In 10 of the 12 attacks, a white shark was the attacker. Barry Wilson was attacked while swimming about 23 metres offshore in 9 metres of water on 7 December 1952, in Monterey Bay. On 7 May 1959, 18-year-old Albert Kogler Jnr was attacked while swimming at Baker Beach, south of the Golden Gate, San Francisco. Both attacks were fatal. Spearfisherman Robert Pamperin was fatally attacked at La Jolla on 18 June 1959.

The increase in attacks off the US coast can be attributed to many factors. The primary factor, however, is the increasing number of people in the ocean: swimmers, divers, abalone divers, spearfishermen, body surfers and surfboard riders taking advantage of wetsuits to offset cooler water temperatures. In some years, such as the El Niño years, the offshore waters are at a higher than normal temperature. The influence of warm water to the north brings a corresponding influx of tropical water species of fish and animals. The incidence of attacks has also increased in other countries with the availability of wetsuits. These suits give body comfort in water once considered too cool for pleasurable swimming, surfing or diving. Humans have thus moved into the cooler water terrritory of the white shark.

In the state of Oregon, six attacks, all by white sharks, have taken place in the period 1926 to 1984. The attacks have been as far north as Cannon Beach near the Washington/Oregon state borders.

The newcomers include the dreaded great white shark. Mr W. I. T. Follett, Curator of Fishes of the Californian Academy of Sciences in San Francisco and the authority on sharks in California, thought a white shark was responsible for the killing of Albert Kogler, whilst Conrad Limbaugh, who investigated the fatal attack at La Jolla, concluded a similar shark killed Robert Pamperin. Observations by swimmers and detailed investigations by scientists from the Stanford University Hopkins Marine Station have also left little doubt that one of the same species was Barry Wilson's killer.

Giving evidence at the inquiry into Albert Kogler's death, Mr Follett said he estimated the shark which killed Albert Kogler must have been at least 3 to 3.5 metres long and to have weighed between 225 and 450 kilograms. White sharks, he said, were not uncommon now along the Pacific coast as far north as Washington State. They appeared over a wide area, but seldom came inshore.

It is worth noting at this point that shark incidents on the west coast have occurred during most months of the year. The sharks here appear to make no attempt to follow the timetable, observed so religiously by their confrères on the east coast or to obey the warm water law, which sharks in most other parts of the world appear to follow. Two attacks, for instance, took place in Monterey Bay during the months of December and February, when sea temperatures are at their lowest. On the east coast attacks at this latitude would only be expected between May and September.

Why sharks on the east coast follow a timetable and those on the west do not is hard to understand. It may be that, as in Australian waters, it is the white shark which contributes the unknown factor in the attack pattern along the west coast, which abounds with seals and sea lion colonies.

In keeping with the observation that shark attacks on any coast are usually concentrated in the vicinity of the most heavily populated areas, the attacks in Northern California have centred on San Franciso and nearby Monterey Bay whilst the attacks in Southern California have been in the region of Los Angeles, La Jolla and San Diego.

In the period 1929 through to the end of 1984, twenty-six attacks took place along the coast and the nearby islands from San Francisco to Los Angeles, and a further six attacks took place in the San Diego area.

In the San Francisco area, although a boy and his dog had been attacked near a canning factory in San Franciso Bay in 1926, swimmers in Northern California regarded themselves as safe until the fatal attack on Barry Wilson in Monterey Bay on 7 December 1952. This attack caught Californians by surprise. It was well above the northern limit of expected attacks.

Another attack in this area was reported on 6 February 1955. In an encounter with a large shark, James F. Jacobs, of Santa Cruz, escaped with little more than some shock and a few gashes to his right foot. The victim in this case was spearfishing.

After this last attack a reward was offered for the first great white shark or man-eater landed from Monterey Bay. The reward was collected a month later by two commercial fishermen who were harpooning basking sharks off Moss Landing on Monterey Bay. They found the shark tearing hunks of flesh from the body of a recently killed 7.5 metre basking shark that they had secured to a buoy while hunting for other baskers. Its overall length was 3.5 metres and the weight was estimated at 350 kilograms.

Four years later, on 7 May 1959, Albert Kogler lost his life in San Francisco Bay. Just over a year later, on 9 May 1960, 16-year-old Suzanne Theriot, splashing with her friends at Hidden Beach near the northern end of Monterey Bay, received such severe injuries in a shark attack that she lost her leg.

One of the attacks in the region of San Luis Obispo was a comparatively minor affair at Pismo Beach. A shark scraped against a 10-year-old boy making deep cuts on his body and shoulder. In the second case, the evidence of a shark attack is inconclusive. On 28 April 1957, Peter Savino, aged 25, was swimming with a friend against a strong tide in Morro Bay. His friend said Savino was hanging on to him. There was a sudden swirl; Savino called out, "Something has hit me," and held up a bloody arm. He disappeared and his body was never recovered. Next day, coastguards searching for his body sighted a 6 metre shark.

Robert Lee and Daniel Miller in their paper "Shark Attacks off the California and Oregon Coast, an update 1980 to 1984" list only eight attacks from the Los Angeles, Orange County and San Diego areas.

Sea lions also abound in these waters, but the general opinion is that they were not responsible for any of these attacks. It is possible, however, that they may influence the activities of sharks in the area.

These sea lions are big and extremely fast in the water. They provide added spice to the underwater excitement of skindivers in the area and are liable to scare the wits out of inexperienced divers. They are said to have teeth like a horse and be able to butt like a battering ram. Usually friendly and curious, once in a while they become belligerent and attack. One is reported to have ripped open the back of a La Jolla diver. An expert diver said he had observed hundreds of them underwater without being injured, but he always treated them with respect.

The fatal attacks on Albert Kogler at San Francisco and on Robert Pamperin at La Jolla occurred within the space of five weeks. They caused great consternation throughout California.

The attack on Albert Kogler received worldwide notice. It was remarkable for the outstanding courage of a young woman, Shirley O'Neill.

A 5.30 p.m. on 7 May 1959 at Baker's Beach in San Francisco Bay, 18-year-old Albert Kogler and Shirley O'Neill were together about 50 metres from the shore.

Shirley O'Neill's graphic statement to the press revealed the details of the tragedy and what went on in the mind of the intrepid woman during some terrible moments.

After saying she and Albert sunned for a few minutes and then went into the water, she added:

We'd been in for about fifteen minutes and were out maybe 40 or 50 yards [about 40 metres], when he said:

"We're out pretty far now, let's go no farther, it'd be too dangerous."

We were treading water as we were talking. We were just

about to start back and I was looking away from him towards the Golden Gate [to the east], when I heard him scream.

I turned around and saw this big thing flap up into the air. I didn't know whether it was a fin or a tail. I knew it was some kind of a fish.

There was a threshing in the water and I knew he was struggling with it. It must have been pretty big.

He shouted "It's a shark . . . get out of here."

I started swimming back. I swam a few strokes, but then I thought to myself, "I can't just leave him here."

I was scared and I didn't know what to do, but I knew I couldn't leave him.

I turned round and took a couple of strokes back.

He kept screaming. I could tell the fish was chewing him up. It was a horrible scream.

All I could see was blood all over the water.

He was shouting "Help me! Help me!"

Unaided, with superb courage and almost superhuman effort, she struggled for twenty minutes and brought him almost to the shore when a fisherman threw her a line and pulled them the rest of the way.

On the beach Shirley O'Neill prayed over the dying youth and remained with him until an ambulance took him to hospital. Three hours later he died.

Five weeks later on the afternoon of 14 June 1959, at La Jolla, a shark attacked and killed Robert Pamperin, a 33-year-old engineer spearfishing approximately 60 metres north of Alligator Head. The following description of the attack is extracted from an article in the magazine *The Skin Diver*, August 1959, by Conrad Limbaugh, head diver of the Scripps Institute of Oceanography. Limbaugh was, until his unfortunate death, widely known as America's foremost and most experienced scuba diver.

The victim, who was diving for abalone with a partner, was wearing blue fins, a pink bathing suit, black face mask and a pair of gloves. In addition he carried a yellow-handled abalone iron and was pushing an inflated black inner tube, to which a burlap sack was attached.

They started out from a rocky point and were about 45 metres from the shore when the partner, who was a less experienced diver, decided to work closer to the shore. When about 15 metres away, he heard Pamperin call out "Help me!"

Turning, he saw Pamperin thrown upright out of the water with his face mask missing. Pamperin then disappeared. The partner swam towards where he had last seen Pamperin and looking down through his face mask, he saw Pamperin held about the waist in the jaws of a shark he estimated to be about 6 metres long. The shark was jerking its head and lashing its tail and refused to be frightened by the rescuer's attempts to scare it off. The partner then swam ashore and gave the alarm.

About this time, Conrad Limbaugh arrived on the scene. With nine volunteers he put in four and a half hours scuba diving in the immediate vicinity. Visibility was about 6 metres and the sea temperature 20°C. They found no trace of Pamperin, although a helicopter saw a blue fin floating in the water and the victim's float with two abalone in it was found some distance away.

Some fish had been speared in the area shortly before the attack and a beaked whale had come ashore about a kilometre away. Several killer whales had been seen in the area on the same day. Conrad Limbaugh carefully sifted all the evidence and concluded that Pamperin's killer was a great white shark.

White sharks have been a problem to divers along the west coast, particularly in southern California. The area is not regularly populated by the warm water species of whalers and tigers. Most of the sharks are the cooler water species: blue sharks, porbeagles, threshers, occasional makos and, of course, the great white sharks. This latter species acts as it does everywhere — attacking strongly, savagely and fatally.

On the California–Oregon coast, there were 36 attacks on humans from 1952 to 1982, as follows: 1952 — 1; 1955 — 1; 1959 — 2; 1960 — 2; 1961 — 2; 1962 — 1; 1964 — 1; 1966 — 1; 1968 — 1; 1969 — 2; 1972 — 3; 1974 — 5; 1975 — 4; 1976 — 3; 1977 — 1; 1979 — 2; 1980 — 1; 1982 — 3.

Two attacks on the west coast took place on the same day, 30 September 1984, but these attacks were not by the same shark, as they were some 800 kilometres apart. Both these attacks were non-fatal and both were by white sharks.

In the first attack, a free-diving abalone diver, Paul Parsons, was diving just south of Tomales Point north of San Francisco. In this area six skindivers had been attacked over the years, making it the area with the highest number of shark attacks on the California coast. All these attacks were on abalone divers. Five of the victims suffered major injury but immediate first-aid and speedy application of medical treatment saved all the attacked.

Paul Parsons was diving from an inflatable boat when he felt "uncomfortable". He called to his tenders on the boat to pick him up as well as his companion Mike Eccles. He dived again to fill in the time while the boat came to him and had returned to within 3 metres of the surface when he was bitten from behind by a large white shark. He tried to hit it with his abalone-collecting iron while the shark shook him. It then let him go, allowing Parsons to swim to the boat, where the bleeding was controlled, and forty minutes later he was in intensive care in hospital.

That same day, at 3.30 p.m., Robert Rice was riding his surfboard 770 kilometres away at Cape Kawanda, Oregon, when a white shark suddenly struck at his board, biting it twice and then swimming away.

Half a minute before Rice had been lying flat on his board and if attacked in this position would most probably have lost his right arm and shoulder and suffered the same fate as Lewis Boren. Boren disappeared on the afternoon of 19 December 1981 at Spanish Bay, Monterey. Two surfers walking the beach found his board in two pieces 15 metres apart, then five days later a body was found floating a kilometre north at Spanish Bay, and subsequently identified as Lewis Boren.

Examination of the clean cuts through the board, the body and the wetsuit indicated that the surfer had been in a prone position on the board with arms outstretched when attacked. The first attack was savage and powerful and Boren probably slipped from the board. A second less violent bite on the board or a repositioning of the board in the shark's jaws was indicated by impressions forward of the main bite that chopped surfer and board. Although the body of Lewis Boren was in the water for 115 hours and initially there would have been a tremendous flow of blood, he was only bitten once.

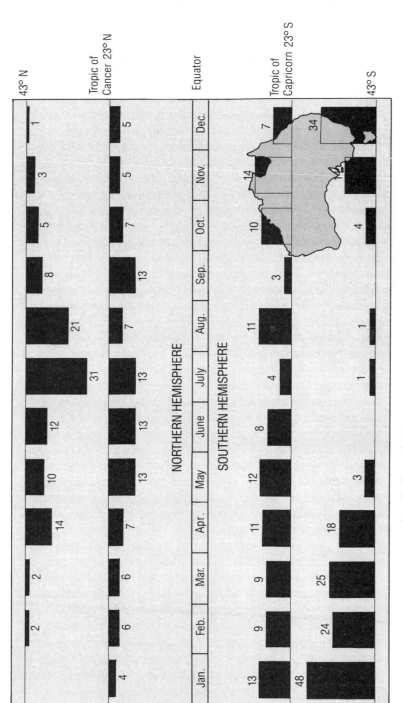

Months of attack in Northern and Southern Hemispheres.

PART IV

OTHER EXPERIENCES WITH SHARKS AND METHODS OF DEFENCE

SKINDIVERS, SPEARFISHERMEN AND SHARKS

The development of underwater swimming and spearfishing on its modern scale has added to the number of humans in the water, particularly in more isolated areas. Records from many parts of the world tell of sharks attacking spearfishermen and underwater swimmers, and in a later section will be found references to a number of attacks.

The growth in skindiving and spearfishing worldwide has resulted in an increase in the number of attacks as well as increase in the known attack localities. This factor, along with the increase in cool water attacks, resulting from swimmers, surfers and commercial and sport divers moving into the white shark's habitat, are two features of changing shark attack in modern times. The more man moves into the shark's domain then the greater the spread and variation in attacks.

Prior to the buildup of cooler water attacks on divers and spearfishermen, more than half of all shark attacks took place less than 60 metres from shore (the area in which most humans swim and surf). The remainder were almost evenly split between 60 and 1600 metres offshore, and in the open ocean. Divers have changed these statistics as this activity has become more popular. David Baldridge's analysis of attacks in the Shark Attack File revealed that 25 per cent of victims were taking part in underwater activities and that of the attacked, 43 per cent were free diving.

Attacks by white sharks have taken place in cooler waters even down as low as 1°C as well as in the tropical waters (the home of the tigers and whalers) right up to 34°C.

Spearfishing can be regarded as provocation of sharks because the panic and injured vibrations and blood and slime from speared fish are all attractants.

In his book *Shark Attack Against Man*, Dr Baldridge listed 244 records of shark attacks on divers, more than one fifth of his entire shark attack file, and predicted because of the growth of diving activities this percentage could grow to at least one third. He noted that in 1967 more than half of the twenty-eight reported attacks were on divers. Despite the benefits of improved underwater vision from their face masks, statistics show that in 43 per cent of the attacks sharks were not seen before the attack. The Shark Attack File statistics show that carcharhinids (whalers/bull sharks) were responsible for 28 per cent of all attacks on divers on the surface and 26 per cent of the attacks on submerged divers. Tiger shark attacks were next, with 13 per cent of the diver attacks, and 10 per cent on submerged divers, while white sharks were third, with 12 per cent of diver attacks and 17 per cent of the attacks on submerged divers. Of the attacked divers, 43 per cent were snorkellers or skindivers with mask, snorkel and fins. Scuba divers were next highest on the list of attacks.

The American publication *The Skin Diver* canvassed the leading underwater swimmers of the world for an account of their experiences with sharks.

Jack Ackerman, one of them, believes that blood and movement are the greatest attractions to a shark. He found them cautious to the point of almost being cowards when not incited by the smell of fresh blood or a fish in trouble. When carrying a fish on a spear or stringer, the diver will first notice a shark slowly circling him at a distance. This means the creature has smelt blood or has detected the vibrations sent out through the water by the struggles of the wounded fish.

Consequently it is not going to leave the area. It will get more excited every minute and work its way in closer to the diver with each sweep. The diver now resembles someone teasing a dog. The shark will grow bolder and braver and can become dangerous if the diver does not apply commonsense to the situation.

Famed skindiver Gerd von Dincklage-Schulenberg, who skindived for some years in Sri Lanka, in an account of his experiences, said he had encountered innumerable sharks of various species in ten years of skindiving. He learned at least one thing about them — never take sharks for granted. He wrote:

*They are one of the sea's greatest dangers because they are
more a potential rather than an actual danger to a diver,
which leads to a disregard of them that can be fatal.*

*I have been dismissed contemptuously by such famed killers
as the blue shark, only to have an insignificant white fin make
an all-out attack on me for the sake of my catch. All I can say
about sharks is watch them always and never let them get the
initiative in an attack if you can help it.*

One fishing expert from Venezuela said: "We hear a lot of
stories from the natives about swimmers being attacked by sharks
here but so far we have not been able to authenticate any of
them."

Bill Barada of Southern California, another overseas skindiver
of note, believes that creatures in the ocean are just like animals
on the land. Some sharks, he says, will attack, but most won't
and they don't even know what they will do themselves.

After years of study, Jim Oetzel, another Californian, summed
up his views on sharks in the waters of the western American
coastline. He said the shark menace seems to vary with geo-
graphical areas and certain conditions such as tide and seasonal variations:

*A universal rule would seem to be that remaining in an area
with refuse or bloody or crippled fish is a definite menace, and
many harmless sharks can turn killers in such conditions.
Threatening movements, shouting, splashing or a companion
diving on an onrushing shark have in most cases been effective
in frightening them off. However, sharks are unpredictable
and in a group of excited sharks any method, except getting
out of the water, is suicidal. I believe if a victim has been bitten the shark will return to the original prey.*

Rodney Jonklaas, Assistant Superintendent of the Zoological
Gardens in Sri Lanka and a spearfisherman of experience, made
some interesting comments on the sharks that roam the Sri
Lankan waters: "I have often been rushed by sharks for the fish
I carried about my waist, but the moment I aimed my gun they
kept well out of range. I agree with Hans Hass about sharks in
general. They are cowardly, though cunning, swift, voracious."

Another authority was Herman Echavarria, a spearfisherman from the Caribbean. In eight years he only once had trouble from sharks.

Echavarria's advice was: "Stay near the boat at all times. When danger appears, jump in the boat and give the fish to the shark."

In Australia, along the coastal waters of New South Wales, the relationship of sharks and skindivers is also being carefully studied by underwater research groups and others. Numerous reports from underwater swimmers of their experiences indicate that they only occasionally meet large sharks. Most that they meet are small and timid.

The commonest sharks met are the harmless Port Jackson sharks — rarely more than 1.2 metres long — which are usually found lying in heaps in depressions on rocky bottoms at about 5 to 20 metres. Occasionally school sharks about 1.5 metres long cruising in groups and "gummies", another small and harmless species, are seen. The gummy derives its name from the peculiar flat, pavement-like teeth with which nature has provided it to crush the oysters, crabs and other shellfish it uses for food.

The sharks best known to spearfishermen are wobbegongs and carpet sharks. These grow to a length of 1.5 to 2.5 metres and can easily be recognised by the beard-like process hanging around their mouths as well as their dappled skin. The wobbegong is common among rocks along the New South Wales coast. It occasionally causes injuries with its cruel curved teeth. These attacks are not necessarily from wobbegongs which have been teased or provoked, though in some cases they may have been. Wobbegongs are undoubtedly attracted to spearfishermen by fish they are carrying. The wobbegong is reputed to be most active just about dusk. The carpet shark — so-called because of the design of its skin — looks like a wobbegong, but is larger and more ornate.

Australian sharks have been accused of having a more developed curiosity and killer instinct than sharks in most other parts of the world. Dr Hans Hass, when he visited Australia some years ago with camera and spear, quickly came to the conclusion that the local ones are more dangerous than those of other waters.

On his arrival in Australia, Dr Hass declared a swimmer could frighten off a shark by shouting at it. Later, after meeting a few local selachians face to face, he spoke more reservedly:

The sharks I saw came very close and showed none of the hesitation or wariness of sharks in the Caribbean or Red Sea. Sometimes they came so close they had to be held off with spears. As soon as they found us they would swim towards us without hesitation. I can now better understand the number of shark attacks in Australian waters. However, my wife and I have several times driven off sharks which came dangerously close by shouting at them. Almost all the photographs of sharks I have taken in the Barrier Reef were head on. In the Caribbean and Red Sea, pictures were taken from the side. The less impetuous sharks there did not swim so directly towards us.

Spearfishermen and other underwater swimmers in Australia, however, appear to have no more to fear from sharks than their fellows in most other parts of the world.

One of Australia's most experienced skindivers and active spearfishermen, Don Linklater, has often come face to face with them. He has swum close to some which would not go away, seen others which fled when they saw him and found others that sneaked up behind him. At times he had a suspicion he was the object of attention of many others hovering just out of sight.

Ross Murphy, another experienced Sydney skindiver, says this of the sharks he has met:

The main point I have noticed about sharks is that they are reluctant to come near. Only twice have I seen them approach a man, and that was when a speared fish was struggling violently to get free. The sharks darted at the struggling fish and then shot away without getting it. Whenever I have seen sharks it is always after we have speared a lot of fish. We never see them coming. They simply suddenly arrive. They then usually circle around or stay in the immediate area for about half an hour or more.

Mr R. H. Barton, a former president of the Underwater Spearfishermen's Association of New South Wales, had this to say:

Over a period of ten years we have learned from practical experience that sharks do not ferociously attack every human they see. Their behaviour in all cases is like that of a cur dog;

*if you face up to them, remaining cool and immobile they will
stop, look, and slowly swim away. Sudden movement or
shouting will scare them off. If you show signs of panic, and
thrash the water with arms and legs flailing, they will attack.
Our association has issued this advice to members: When a
fish is speared, do not attach it to your person, but take it
right out of the water immediately.*

The dangers to Australian spearfishermen have been highlighted by the cool water attacks. The stories of the survivors
such as Brian Rodger, Henri Bource and Rodney Fox clearly
illustrate the power of the big hunting sharks, as do the fearful
wounds of the less fortunate spearfishermen, Robert Bartle,
Geoffrey Corner and John Willis. The fastening of speared fish
to 15 metres or more of nylon cord or craypot floats certainly
helps to keep the catch away from the spearfishermen, but
despite this precaution fatalities still occur. Of course, the safest
way is to remove the struggling, bloody fish from the water
immediately. If this is not possible, then the float is the next
best thing.

Most skindivers and writers on skindiving believe, and attack
statistics show, that divers are most likely to be attacked
at or near the surface. They advise divers to go underwater
when sharks are prowling. They say dangerous sharks, being
scavengers, are used to snapping up anything floating on the
surface and that irregular movements of swimmers on the surface
attract sharks' attention. The available evidence does not support
this one way or the other. Divers have reported sharks to a depth
of 80 metres. The greatest depth at which a diver reported being
menaced was 20 metres. At this depth, Earl Murray of the
Scripps Institute, La Jolla, said a shark made a pass at him.

Two, at least, of the attacked Australian fishermen, Rodney
Fox and Robert Bartle, were fully submerged and diving down
when they were attacked.

Time alone will tell whether divers' clothing or its colour has
any effect on a shark. Reports of attacks by sharks on skindivers
rarely refer to the dress or costume of the diver.

In this regard reference might be made to the British Col-
umbia Safety Council's request to its 10,000 skindivers that they
wear pink, yellow and red costumes. In their view skindivers

run less risk of being bitten by sharks than of being speared by their friends. Divers in grey rubber suits have been mistaken for seals and aqualung divers for baby whales.

Experiments by Dr Walter Stark appeared to indicate that wetsuits banded in the manner of sea-snakes in black and white inhibited the approach and activity of sharks under water. But more recent experiments by Valerie Taylor indicated that such banding did not have a deterrent effect.

A number of reports refer to attacks on snorkel divers. In some instances the snorkel itself appears to have attracted the shark's attention. But whether sharks prefer to attack snorkel or other divers rather than scuba divers, the records do not disclose.

The experience of Theo Watts Brown, aged 25, who, in March 1955 at Woodman Point, Western Australia, wearing an aqualung, attempted to break the world's underwater endurance record, gives some interesting sidelights on this matter. He was sitting in 3 metres of water on a 44 gallon drum filled with rocks and was holding a searchlight and a compressed air gun.

At 9 p.m., after he had been down four hours, he saw a shark. He discharged compressed air through the gun and the sudden appearance of the bubbles frightened it away.

At 11.55 p.m., he was standing before the drum, shining his powerful light through the water, when the shark (the same one he thought) rushed him from the side.

Describing his experiences, Brown said:

> It came very fast and I just got the light on it in time. I swung the spear gun around and fired, but it did not stop the shark.
> Somehow the shark bent the spear, which was made of $\frac{3}{8}$-inch [95 millimetre] high grade steel. Still it came on.
> It knocked the drum over and tore one leg of my diving dress.

The shark went away but Brown continued to lie on the bottom for some time before surfacing. He was suffering severely from shock. His main reason for staying down was that he thought he risked further attack if he surfaced.

Most of the attacks have been on divers with fish in the vicinity, on their belts, spears, or floats, or being towed or speared nearby, or fish being cleaned. In one instance a shark even jumped out of the water and took off the arm of a man walking along a reef together with the fish he was carrying. In a number of instances, lobsters instead of fish were the attraction.

Owing to their preoccupation with fishes, sharks naturally take a special interest in spearfishing competitions. In Australia, they are regular spectators at these contests and participating spearfishermen holding fish are never surprised to find they have a shark for a companion.

At an the Australian Spearfishing Championships held at Point Henry, near Bremer Bay, on the south coast of Western Australia, the local sharks certainly added to the excitement of the contest, but no one was actually attacked or hurt. There were, however, a number of scares. Two of the competitors, Brian Marsh and Phil Smith, said they found they were being circled by a 2 metre shark. They shouted at it and it immediately made off, only to return later with a reinforcement in the shape of a larger shark — a 3 metre one. This time, shouting did not work and, followed by the circling sharks, they gradually edged their way to the shore and safety 65 metres away.

Others had similar experiences. Dave Panting of Sydney had just speared a drummer when he received a hard smack on the side. He though it was merely the death struggles of three fish he had on his belt. He was amazed, however, to see a big shark — which he estimated at nearly 3 metres — appear and snatch the drummer struggling on the end of his spear.

John Mitchell of South Australia lost half a 7 kilogram groper to another shark. When the shark returned for the other half Mitchell discreetly let him have it.

An Australian junior champion, 17-year-old Arthur Taylor, however, was determined not to lose his title to a 2 metre shark which tried to wrest a large blue groper from his spear.

Many other competitors saw sharks up to nearly 4 metres long, but were not troubled by them, although in a number of cases the sharks circled or followed them. The opinions of competitors varied concerning the effect of splashing and shouting in frightening the sharks.

In one Australian Pacific Coast Championship, competing fishermen reported seeing more than a hundred sharks. They did not attack or show any interest in the proceedings. In fact, one man is said to have found himself amongst fifty sharks (the biggest was 5 metres) but they took no notice of him. There have been similar stories from other Australian championship competitions.

Examination of the reports of these competitions supports the adage that there is safety in numbers. The sharks prefer to attack lone individuals and in most instances they were obviously after the fish and not the man. The records contain no instance of a spearfisherman being killed by a shark during a competition, but there have been some very narrow escapes.

Serious injury was sustained by Leonard Higgins, 28 years, at Tea Gardens north of Newcastle, New South Wales, in April 1958. Higgins was competing in the Australian Anglers' Spearfishing Championship and was towing some fish on a line about 3 metres behind him, swimming just beneath the surface in water about 3 metres deep and about 20 metres from the shore. A shark struck him from behind, knocking him sideways a metre or so. Nearby a spearfisherman had harpooned a flathead which was flapping on his spear. Higgins swam ashore unaided with a large deep curved wound on the outer side of his left thigh with strips of skin across it looking like the strings of a harp and a few irregular abrasions on the front right side of his abdomen.

On 3 January 1951 at Windang near the entrance to Lake Illawarra on the New South Wales south coast, 20-year-old Albert Pride of Waterloo, Sydney, pitted himself against the savage onslaughts of a large shark for five minutes and was lucky to come out of the one-sided encounter alive. He was spearfishing off a rock island when he sighted a shark coming at him. He was treading water, with a fish speared on the end of his harpoon. Three times the shark circled the petrified man before it charged. Never once did it take its eyes from him. At each circle Pride moved a little closer to the rocks until his body touched the comparative safety of a tiny island.

It would be impossible to tell the story of the struggle that followed more graphically than the victim himself. He said:

When I reached the rocks, I panicked and decided to make a break for the shore about 50 yards [45 metres] away. About halfway there the shark came at me again. I struggled in the water with it for at least five minutes. I kept stabbing at its face with a blunt pocket knife I used to gut my fish. Every

*time I lunged the shark reared up and blood welled in the
water. My thigh was torn and aching.*

*When the shark came close again, it cut a gash across my
chest with its fin and then swam away trailing blood. I
thought I was right and made for the shore again. When
about 40 feet [12 metres] away I heard a terrific noise behind
me. The next thing I remember was the shark rushing between
my legs and I felt myself being hurled forward. I remember
flying through the air across the water and seeing the rocks on
the foreshore coming up, then everything went blank.*

Pride lay unconscious on the rocks for nearly an hour. When
he regained his senses he saw the shark still cruising about. He
staggered, dazed and bleeding from deep lacerations to the left
thigh and chest, across sand dunes to Windang Reserve, where
he collapsed at the feet of some campers.

Shark hunting is becoming the underwater counterpart of
big game hunting. It requires sound underwater knowledge,
control of equipment, clear water and plenty of nerve. It is not
a sport for the inexperienced.

Wally Gibbins of Manly, New South Wales, is a well-known
and experienced diver and expert shark hunter, who has had
numerous encounters with sharks. For shark hunting he works
in a team with three or four others. They dive from a boat and
spear some fish to attract the sharks. When they sight a shark
they swim in formation towards it until they are about 5 metres
away, when they fire a spear into its head or gills. Attached to
the spear is a length of steel rope connected to a partly inflated
inner tube which is used as a float. They then regain the boat
and follow the float. When the shark is exhausted, they haul
it in, tie it to the boat and look for another shark.

The powerhead or "smokey" has given the underwater shark
hunter a most effective weapon. In the hands of expert spear-
men large sharks fall victim, as the kill of Wally Gibbins' 350
kilogram tiger and John Harding's 180 kilogram white shark
clearly prove. As with other dangerous weapons, there is the
strong possibility of powerheads doing even more damage than
a shark attack, and stories are told of inexperienced youths
floundering in the surf with these lethal weapons with the safety
pin removed. In the meantime, however, they have proved their

power against sharks around the world and all the dangerous species, except, perhaps, the mako (blue pointer), have fallen to its lethal blast.

When asked in an interview whether he was afraid of sharks, Wally Gibbins said:

> *You are always frightened, but you get to know the time to be really scared. You can tell by the way the shark is acting when it is time to go for your life. I have found the best thing to do is to draw yourself up, wait until the shark is about 5 feet [1.5 metres] away, then fling out your arms and legs and shout.*
> *The nearer the shark, the more effective is the shouting.*

Until the studies and statistics of the Shark Attack File, little was known about sharks and skindivers, but a growing literature and universal reports from divers, skindiving and spearfishing clubs are assisting the accumulation of information about the relationship between sharks and divers, the precautions skindivers should take and the defensive measures they should adopt.

In his book *Skin Diving in Australia* an expert skindiver, Edwin du Cros, sums up the risks to skindivers and stresses the importance of always being prepared for shark attacks. He says experience has shown that our early fears that sharks might prove a major deterrent to skindiving were groundless. Sharks and men have had so many bloodless encounters that the shark has lost something of its reputation for ferocity. Skindivers stand much less chance of being attacked than most other swimmers.

This does not mean, however, the sharks are harmless, that knowledge of them by skindivers is not essential or that safety rules can at any time be ignored.

It is also generally agreed by divers that those without great experience would at all times be well advised in shark waters to adopt the bodyguard or buddy system or go below in groups with a line to the surface and take some means of protection. Most accidents to skindivers have happened when diving alone. Spearfishermen holding fishes and especially lobsters should take particular care.

Reference has already been made to Bruce Wright, who commanded a British shallow-water diving unit during the war. His views are that any shark is likely to molest a swimmer, but sharks over 2 metres in length must be regarded with suspicion. He found most sharks comparatively harmless. Large and dangerous sharks often were in the vicinity of men swimming but took no notice of them. A shark, he said, which comes up to investigate can often be scared off by hitting it across the snout or even touching its body with a spear. A shark's skin is very tough and the only effective way of getting a spear into it is through the gill slits or by using a heavy-duty spear.

Wright gave advice to underwater swimmers in shark-frequented waters:

> *Carry a knife, spear, or shark billy.*
> *Do not wear or carry anything white.*
> *At night carry shark repellent, don't shine a light underwater and remember every phosphorescent flash in the water is not a shark.*

Similar advice was given by Vernon E. Brock, a former Director of the Fish and Game Division of the Territorial Board of Agriculture and Forestry in Hawaii. He says anyone takes a certain amount of risk when encountering sharks, but they seem only to attack when an extra factor, like dead fish, bleeding in the water or a swimmer's helplessness, encourages an attack.

Mr Brock's hints on what to do when encountering sharks are:

> *Do not keep speared fish next to your body. If you have to, keep them on a line, string them far out behind, so a shark can attack them and not connect you with them. A good rule is to fish with a boat near by, and put the fish in it.*
> *The best bet is to swim in a reefed area that sharks cannot enter. If swimming in deep water, always use a face mask so that if a shark is in the vicinity you can watch him while making your escape.*

Perry Gilbert, Leonard Schultz and Stewart Springer of the American Institute of Biological Sciences Shark Research Panel place the "buddy system" first in their advice to skin and scuba divers. Their advice is:

> *Always dive with a companion.*
> *Do not spear, ride or hang on to the tail of a shark.*

Do not provoke a shark, even a small and seemingly harmless one. It invites possible severe injury.

Remove all speared fish from the water immediately. Do not tow them in a bag or on a line cinched to the waist.

Avoid extremely turbid or dirty water or where underwater visibility is poor.

Certainly, Hugh Edwards' experience of being attacked by a whaler shark off the West Australian coast in 1964 underlines the importance of avoiding murky water. He describes the attack in his book *Islands of Angry Ghosts*:

I dived again, and poised over a volcanolike knoll at the edge of the seventy-foot [20 metre] ledge — dark, evil water misty below me... when the shark appeared on the edge of my vision, coming up out of the deep and moving very fast. I swung to meet him, following the old routine which had proved itself dozens of times before: Stick your speargun out in front; make yourself look as big as possible; growl to convince yourself if you like; then swim right at your shark as though you mean to eat him. He will circle nervously and depart, convinced that you are a dangerous animal.

This shark was the exception.

He stood my bluff with watchful, yellow eyes, and as I closed, turned his pig head up toward me in a horrible, inquiring manner. He was about eight or nine feet [2.5 metres] long, thick as a barrel, with long gill slits — a whaler shark, genus Carcharinus, *with the words "Dangerous to Man" written against his name in text books.*

I ran out of breath — we don't use breathing apparatus when fishing — and ascended to the surface, watching him closely. Suddenly without warning and without any of the usual preliminary circling, he attacked... Somehow I got the gun around and with a controlled effort sent the spear thudding into his side, through his left pectoral fin and out again.

There was no chance to reload.

He swirled me aside in an explosion of muscled power and I tensed for the recoil attack. It didn't come. Instead he sounded down into the black water. I had hurt him more than I thought; he was shaking his ugly head like a groggy boxer

trying to clear his eyes and trailing blood in his wake...
It was my own fault. Swimming alone in dark, deep water
with the sun sinking below the horizon (I had told others
dozens of times when giving advice), was just asking for
trouble.

The Officer in Charge of a British Naval Clearance Diving
Unit who supervised the clearance of explosives from the
approaches to the port of Mombasa also offered some important advice. He reported sharks of various species were observed
both on the surface and underwater. At no time did they attack
or even appear curious, but always made off at their best speed
on sighting. His conclusion was that in reasonable visibility of
about 9 metres a shark will not attack. His advice is:

On jumping into the water swim straight to the bottom
without waiting to make final adjustments to equipment on the
surface.
Do not linger on the surface on completion of a dive whilst
awaiting pick-up by a boat, but sight the boat from
underwater and make straight for the ladder.

Examination of accounts of attacks on skindivers and
swimmers also suggests the following advice and precautions:

Do not wear rings, bright ornaments or white clothing or have
flashing parts on your equipment.
Be on guard in areas where swimmers have been recently
attacked, where fishes are being snatched from fishermen's
lines, dogs being taken or fishing nets being raided.
Take care near the mouths of creeks and rivers after heavy
rain, especially in murky water. In California, experts believe
attacks on spearfishermen are most likely to occur off rocky
points.
Avoid areas where people are fishing from boats, rocks or
beaches and particularly where fishes are being cleaned.
Avoid schools of fish and areas where fishes are jumping or
birds swooping.
Take care swimming around ships in harbours or in the
open sea, especially near portholes where garbage is being
dumped.
Be on guard if small fishes suddenly scatter.

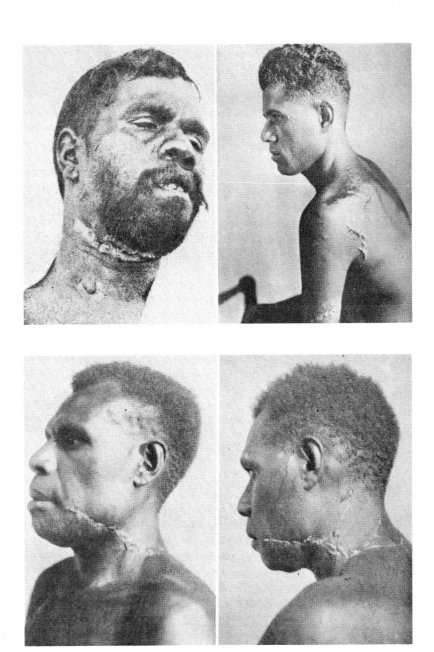

TOP LEFT: *Treacle, who had his head in a shark's mouth.* RIGHT: *J. Messot.*

BOTTOM: *The wounds of the diver Iona Asai, front and side views.*

Unlike birds and fishes, which can see as well behind as forwards, a human is restricted to forward vision. For this reason, many experienced divers in tropical and other shark waters feel safer with their backs to a steep cliff or reef. They are then able to see anything approaching from the front whilst being protected against attack from the rear.

It is impossible, however, to lay down rules for all emergencies. Sharks do not always act in the same way. Sharks vary in their species, habits, dispositions and behaviour. The same sharks may act differently in different areas or at different times of the year. The best advice to beginners is to join a skindiving club before they begin diving. The best guides to diving in any area are a knowledge of its local reputation and peculiarities and the advice of those who have previously dived in the area.

In Australia some skindiving clubs have adopted the practice of the diver raising his left arm on sighting a shark to warn others in the vicinity.

Some spearfishermen, believing that attack is the best form of defence, spear the shark. The result seems to depend upon the shark. Even harmless wobbegongs resent it. Results differ. Some sharks dash off with their spearer for several hundred metres. Others tangle the cord attached to the spear around the person. Careless spearers have at times lost large pieces of skin and parts of their anatomy by allowing sharks they have speared to come too close to them. At times the sharks fasten onto the spearers with a bulldog grip that can only be broken by wrenching or cutting off the shark.

The usual object in spearing the shark is to kill it. Some divers think this is not essential. They believe that once a shark is speared, it will begin to fight the spear. In many instances the spear has bounced off or immediately fallen out, after which the shark has abruptly left.

In at least four instances, spearfishermen have claimed they saved themselves when in difficulties by firing their spears into a shark's open mouth.

Killing a large shark with a spear, however, is far from easy. It needs proper equipment, a powerful gun, a sure aim and the judgment of a toreador. The general rule is, if level with the shark, to fire at its gills or the side of its head. But it is better to be above the shark and hit it square in the middle of its

A blue shark attacking Valerie Taylor in her mesh suit pulls back its nose ready to shake her and use its body weight to try to tear off a piece of flesh.
RON AND VALERIE TAYLOR

forehead just in front of where its head merges into its body. With a well-placed strike here the shark gives a shudder and soon dies.

The powerhead, which uses either a rifle or shotgun cartridge, is the skindiver's best defence against sharks. Using this weapon, Wal Gibbons killed a 3.4 metre tiger shark at Queensland's Heron Island. This shark may be the biggest yet killed by a skindiver with a single shot. Powerheads are also used by fishermen to kill sharks from boats. They are usually used on a hand shaft but can be attached to spears propelled from spearguns. Results have proved that an "explosive" hit on the head with a powerhead quickly kills sharks of the size and species normally encountered by spearfishermen.

Ron and Valerie Taylor have recorded that special stainless steel mesh suits have successfully resisted bites of tropical and temperate water shark species (*Carcharhinus* and school blue sharks). The stainless steel mesh suits gave very good protection and appear able to resist the incredible bite pressure shown by Dr Perry Gilbert to be exerted by sharks at the point of the tooth. But even these super stainless steel mesh suits (which are very expensive) would not solve the problem of the violent shaking that accompanies attacks by the big species, or prevent bruising and internal pressure injuries in attacks by these species.

ATTACKS ON BOATS

Sharks by no means vent their ferocity exclusively on humans. They will, if the mood takes them, attack anything in their way. Boats, for instance, are favourite targets. Large pieces are often torn from various types of boats, launches and in fact practically any floating object. Sharks have made quite a habit of bumping surf skis, chasing skiffs and nipping the blades of oars. Many of the attacks against boats seem to be without reason, but in most cases fishes have been the attraction.

The lengths to which the sharks will go in search of fish are incredible. Urged on by the struggles of the fish, whether caught on lines or in nets, the sharks often attack fishing craft. The smell of fish around the boat, bait in the boat, or even the sound of fishes flapping on the floorboards is enough to excite them. Apparently frantic with hunger, sharks have even at times been known to leap bodily into the boats.

Just before Christmas 1946 Harry Lone, well-known fisherman of Gladstone, Queensland, left his fishing launch moored alongside a jetty while he went to lunch. Later he was about to step into the craft, when, to his amazement, he saw a 180 kilogram shark lying in the cockpit. It had obviously taken a flying leap from the water during his absence. Lone and a friend took a knife to it. The shark retaliated so violently with snapping teeth and flying tail that after it was killed, Lone spent some time sadly examining the launch's bent tail shaft, a broken clutch and smashed floorboards.

Fortunately for fishermen, such marine gymnastics are rare, but when, however, an enterprising shark hurls itself into a small boat occupied by fishermen, fishing becomes really exciting.

With two others, 35-year-old Doug Miller was fishing from a 5 metre dinghy at Seaholme, Victoria, one fine day in December 1949. Miller was not feeling particularly fit — in fact he was lying in the bottom of the dinghy feeling very much out of sorts. Up to this point any amateur fisherman could feel sympathy for Doug Miller. Later he told his story, short and to the point. He said:

> *One minute I was lying there, wishing I was dead. I felt terrible. Suddenly I heard a scream and a yell and an eight-and-a-half-foot [2.6 metre] grey nurse landed fair on top of me. For a second I didn't know what it was. Then I knew and nearly blacked out. I fought to get to my feet and as soon as I did I was knocked down by its tail. Three times I stood up and three times I landed back in the bottom of the boat. I felt like going overboard, but I couldn't leave the other two.*

All three in the boat had great difficulty in avoiding injury from the snapping teeth and threshing tail before they finally killed the shark with a mighty blow from the tiller. Recent research on the grey nurse, however, would indicate that this was another case of mistaken identity.

All kinds of craft have been damaged and sunk and in some cases lives have been lost by sharks' ramming tactics. Even sturdily built boats have been attacked. Some of the attacks by hooked sharks have been particularly savage. At Cronulla, New South Wales, in March 1934, two fishermen caught a 3.5 metre shark on a line about 10 kilometres off the coast. The enraged creature immediately speared into an attack on the solid 5.5 metre launch. Several times it drove its great weight at the launch, snapping viciously at the rudder and bow, causing the boat to rock violently. The two men were mightily relieved to be taken aboard a larger launch. Meanwhile the shark continued its attack on the smaller boat. The shark fought every inch of the way for an hour before it was landed. Several mako shark's teeth were later extracted from the launch's timber.

Game fishing cruisers are often attacked by hungry or angry sharks and their teeth are frequently found embedded in the boat's woodwork. White sharks and makos in particular attack small craft, but tigers and whalers will also cause damage, and create a nuisance. Makos will jump into boats and cause damage, when hooked and fighting, or swimming free. The best advice is to leave them alone to lessen the possibility of crew and craft being damaged.

In other instances sharks have attacked boats because they were molested by the occupants. Two men, A. and E. Norton of Lorne, Victoria, brought a lot of trouble on themselves in this way. They were cruising in their 5 metre motor-launch about 150 metres from the pier at Lorne on Christmas Eve 1935 when they saw a large shark — 4 metres — swimming beside the boat about a metre under the surface. It was undoubtedly the shark which for some weeks had annoyed fishermen near the pier and the week before had killed a seal.

A. Norton decided to deal with it. He lashed a knife to an oar. Then thrusting downwards with all his strength, he stabbed the shark in the back. The water was stained with its blood. The shark reacted immediately; it rose up under the launch, lifted it almost clear of the water and at the same time wriggled itself free of the blade.

Not deterred, Norton made another stab at the monster. The shark promptly replied by stoving in the launch's bow, leaving a hole measuring 50 centimetres by 25 centimetres. Water poured in. The launch immediately filled and began to sink. The two men were left floundering in the water, expecting to be attacked at any moment. They clung to the gunwale for ten minutes, calling out until help came. The shark was not seen again. Whether it was mortally wounded by the knife thrust or whether it injured itself when it charged the boat is not known.

But it is not always so easy to explain why sharks attack boats. What, for instance, attracted the shark that nose-dived like a torpedo at a 5 metre launch 2.5 kilometres off the New South Wales south coast on 7 April 1953? Was it the metal under the boat, bait, or fish in the boat?

The engine had just been started when the shark struck. It hit the boat with such terrific force that it broke one of the boat's ribs, of very strong English ash, in three places. In addition to stoving in two planks the impact is reported to have knocked the shark unconscious.

It is perhaps paradoxical that it is particularly in those areas where attacks on bathers are practically unknown that most of the attacks on boats have occurred. In Spencer Gulf, South Australia, for instance, where the white shark abounds, and on some parts of the coast of New South Wales, it is possible to count on the fingers of one hand the number of attacks on humans. Yet sharks' encounters with boats in these areas make a long and exciting history.

Spencer Gulf is noted for the size of its sharks. An experience G. Nardelli and his son had in April 1946 is typical of some of the attacks by the sharks which inhabit these waters.

Nardelli and his son were fishing from a boat off Port Newby when Nardelli noticed a huge 6 metre shark taking the line. Suddenly it began threshing the water and then for no apparent reason charged the boat. It tore off the rudder, flung it high into the air and savaged it like a mad dog. Then, as if to add insult to injury, it made off with the rudder between its teeth. When Nardelli found his rudder again, it bore numerous teeth marks which had almost perforated the thick wood.

There has even been a South Australian fatality resulting from a white shark attack on a small boat. The victim did not even receive any external wounds from tooth or skin. Leslie Harris and his son Tony were fishing in a small rowing boat about a kilometre offshore in Spencer Gulf near Port Pirie on a summer day in 1971 when a white shark came from the water and almost sank their boat, and tried to come inboard over the gunwale. Tony Harris with his bare hands rolled the attacking shark back into the water as it slashed at them. The shark then prowled under the boat as Tony rowed it to shore and safety, but safety came too late for his father, Leslie, who died from a heart attack before they reached shore.

Other encounters of a different type, some with fatal results, have occurred off the coasts of New South Wales and Victoria and other parts of the world.

Apart from these attacks on boats, it is not unusual for a passing shark to take a bite out of an oar. What inspires such attacks — do they mistake the oar for fish or food, or is it merely a shark's idea of innocent fun?

There is nothing new about this query. In 1865, R. H. Barrett, a pilot, was holding a steering oar in a whaleboat and was about to board a ship off Semaphore, South Australia, when a shark seized the oar and nearly knocked him overboard.

A particularly large shark is also reported to have torn a piece from an oar on 4 March 1936, when the keeper of a lighthouse near Cape Hotham, about 80 kilometres from Darwin, was being rowed ashore. The attack almost wrenched the oar from the hand of the Aborigine rowing the dinghy. It is said the sharks are attracted by the bright copper binding on the blade of the oars. In former days, when copper was widely used for propellers and hulls, there were many stories of sharks damaging them.

Some years ago the schooner *Rachel Cohen* was dry-docked on Jenkins's slip in South Australia. The bilge had more than barnacles on it. There were a number of top and bottom teeth from the mouth of an enormous shark embedded in the vessel's copper-covered planks.

Racing skiffs and canoes also attract sharks, but what it is that attracts them is hard to imagine. There are no fishes or fishing bait. Is it the shine on the wood, metal fittings or colour? Does the shark mistake it for food or an enemy? Does it merely chase it in the same way that a dog chases a car?

A 100-mile [160 kilometre] canoe race held on the Hawkesbury River, New South Wales, on 30 October 1954 is an example. A Victorian crew, Bob Collins and Alan Cosgrove, said a 1.75 metre shark followed them for 2 kilometres, keeping a metre or so from their canoe. They were not the only attraction. Other competitors were escorted by dozens of small sharks racing them over the finishing line.

Similar stories of sharks chasing launches, boats and skiffs are common. In two instances in Australian waters sharks have attacked racing skiffs going at full speed. In both cases the occupants were training for State championships.

On the evening of 30 February 1936, in the Brisbane River, Queensland, a 3 metre shark damaged the outrigger of the Queensland sculling champion, C. E. Slaughter.

Slaughter, skipper of the Commercial Rowing Club, was training for the State championships in a new shell. He was sprinting to the boatshed after sculling 3 kilometres. Almost opposite the Edward Street ferry wharf, he noticed a sudden swirl near the stern. A moment later the shell rocked violently and almost capsized. Slaughter immediately made a dash for the bank. Then he saw the shark. It followed close to the stern for about 20 metres before disappearing. Six metres from the bank, the shell filled and sank. Slaughter got ashore. When he recovered the shell he found a dozen of the shark's teeth on either side. Some had penetrated the wood. The stern was splintered for more than a metre.

In Sydney Harbour, on 1 February 1955, a shark chose a more ambitious target and jumped out of the water in the Parramatta

River to take on a whole racing eight. Sydney Rowing Club senior eight was paddling solidly past the Walker Convalescent Home during one of its training rows for the State championship. There was a swish in the water, then a grey form flew through the air. The No. 2 oar, Dick Brown, suddenly felt the oar ripped from his hands. This, no doubt, broke the shark's leap and it fell into the water about 10 centimetres away from the shell. Bow oar Bill Andrews and Brown saw the creature's tail slashing the water, then it disappeared. The force of the attack swung the shell broadside on, and waves from the shark's impact on the water splashed into the bow end of the eight. Fortunately the only damage, apart from the shocked, nervous condition of the rowers, was Brown's twisted outrigger.

A few days later, about 500 metres from where this incident occurred, a lone sculler, Barry Court, aged 24, was trailed by a 3.5 metre shark. He pulled quickly to the shore with the shark following him. After he left the water the shark circled for twenty minutes.

In February 1929 a more playful shark varied the usual routine by taking charge of a canoe at Glenelg, South Australia, and pushing it from the jetty to a point about 100 metres away. The canoeists were happy to be rescued by a passing yacht from their unenviable predicament.

In Sydney Harbour another massive shark scared the wits out of two young boys fishing off Ball's Head in a heavy rowing boat. The boys, on their way home, had just turned into Berry's Bay when their boat was suddenly lifted violently a foot out of the water and nearly turned over. The youngsters thought they had hit a partly submerged log. Then the "log", all 4.5 metres of its long grey shape, shot from beneath the boat, circled and disappeared.

Harbour incidents with sharks, however, are not common. Residents of Sydney have often wondered why people clinging to overturned sailing boats in Sydney Harbour seem to have such a charmed life where sharks are concerned. When there is a good stiff breeze on the harbour on any Saturday afternoon during the sailing season, a capsized boat, as the records show, will not even attract the attention of a shark. Not once has a crew member, waiting in the water for rescue, been attacked. Indeed there have been very few recorded incidents connected with sharks and overturned boats in Sydney Harbour.

SHIPWRECK AND OTHER
SEA SURVIVORS
AND SHARKS

It is the experience of all who have voyaged leisurely by raft in tropical waters that sharks constantly follow them. The sharks trail the rafts and circle them night and day with little let-up in their menacing vigil. In the account of his famous voyage of 101 days on the raft *Kon-Tiki* across the east Pacific from Peru to Tahiti, Thor Heyerdahl wrote of his ghastly escort:

We had not been long at sea, before the first visited us, and sharks soon became an almost daily occurrence. Sometimes the sharks just came swimming up to inspect the raft and went off in search of prey after circling round us once or twice. But most often the sharks took up a position in our wake just behind the steering oar and there they lay without a sound, stealing from starboard to port and occasionally giving a wag of their tails to keep pace with the raft's placid advance.

George Burton, one of those adventurous souls who like to keep the world an interesting place by doing unusual things, had a similar experience. In 1955 he constructed a home-made 9 metre ketch and set off alone through the Azores, a mere 3500 kilometres, and then, because he liked the life, continued on to Gibraltar. Practically the whole of the distance he was watched and closely followed by sharks and, at times, some inquisitive whales.

During World War II crashed airmen, shipwreck survivors and others who were forced to spend long periods adrift in boats, rafts and similar flimsy craft in tropical seas had similar experiences. They found that although sharks often did little harm, they were a constant menace and added greatly to their hardships.

Just a few days before the surrender of Singapore in 1942,

three men, Bombardier J. Hall, Private Green, of the Sherwood Foresters and Captain C. O. Jennings, RE Anti-tank Regiment, escaped to Sumatra, where they managed to acquire a clinker-built dinghy, 5 metres long and 1.4 metres in the beam. The dinghy had three seats and a tiny tiller cockpit. In this craft, with little experience in navigation, they proposed to reach Australia, nearly 2600 kilometres away. They endured 125 days on the open sea before sighting land, only to find themselves back in Sumatra, 190 kilometres from the spot they had left more than three months before.

Sharks, indirectly, almost drove them to madness. It was hot and oppressive in the small open craft, wallowing on a breathless sea. Their constant obsession was to dive overboard and cool themselves in the inviting water. But there were sharks there — sharks were always there. Day after day their shadows, the sharks, followed the boat, lazing along just a couple of yards behind the tiller. On one occasion when the men lit a fire to prepare a meal, a shark shot at the boat and hit it with such terrific force that it smashed the rudder.

In *Merchantmen at War*, the official story of the Merchant Navy, R. H. Wilson, chief engineer of a vessel that went down in the Atlantic Ocean two degrees south of the Equator, describes twelve days adrift on a raft with sixteen others.

There were three rafts roped together. As they drifted through the long days and nights they were surrounded continually by sharks, varying from a metre or so in length to nearly 3 metres. The smaller ones were always there, but the big fellows were seen mostly at daybreak and sunset. During the war, such stories were common and even those in the comparative safety of ship's boats, as the following account shows, were not entirely free from the sharks' attentions.

When a German U-boat sent a salvo of torpedoes into the hull of the *City of Cairo*, five days out from Cape Town, on 2 October 1942, the entire complement took to the lifeboats and rafts and headed for St Helena. Angus McDonald was in a ship's boat packed with fifty-four survivors. Extracts from his log referred to sharks:

> *Before noon on that first day we saw our first sharks. They were enormous and as they glided backwards and forwards under the boat it seemed they would hit and capsize us. They*

just skimmed the boat each time and they were never to leave us all the time we were in the boat. . . A few more Lascars died during the night and we had to bury them at daybreak. The sharks were there in shoals that morning and the water was churned up as they glided backwards and forwards near the bodies. On the fifteenth day one of the firemen jumped over the stern. He had forgotten to take off his life jacket, and as we were now too weak to turn the boat round to save him, the sharks got him before he could drown.

Later the survivors were taken aboard a German vessel, *Rhakotis*, bound for Bordeaux. *Rhakotis* was rendezvousing with a number of U-boats when she was fired on by a British cruiser. The crew scuttled their vessel and the survivors from the *City of Cairo* were packed on board a U-boat.

During the war such stories were common. One of the grimmest concerns an American vessel which received a torpedo amidships some 160 kilometres off the South American coast. The ship went to the bottom and dozens of survivors took to the boats and rafts. A seaman named Izzy survived 83 days on a raft. There are few tales to equal the terror of those long days he spent in shark-infested waters.

In an account of his experiences, Izzy said:

You could hear guys hollering for help as the ship went down, screaming that sharks were attacking them and there was nothing you could do, and then maybe they would stop screaming and you wouldn't hear them after that or maybe a guy would stop screaming right in the middle of a yell and you would know that something certainly got him.

Sharks were continually around the raft and when they got too close they were driven away with whacks on the nose with a pole from the men clinging desperately to the frail bamboo. Some of the men nevertheless swam unmolested from one raft to the other.

Sharks in other ways added to the torments suffered by survivors in rafts and open boats as they sat scorched by a blazing sun and surrounded by the limitless ocean. Always there was that almost overpowering maddening obsession to dive in and cool themselves in the tantalising salt water—had it not been for the sharks.

When the British vessel *Empire Avocet* went down during the war the second officer took charge of a small raft built on empty oil drums, carrying a number of the crew. The officer's log refers to their hardships:

> *During the afternoon calms, when the heat is intense, men have asked if they can go overboard. So far I have not allowed it for fear of sharks. . . However I decided it was better to take risks than to have men going mad with thirst. It was organized so that there were never more than three in the water at once, while the rest kept a look-out for sharks. They were always somewhere in the vicinity. Every day each of the men spent a little time in the water with a rope around his waist. This was held by the others. The men holding the rope kept a look-out and when they saw a quick grey form approaching they would jerk their companion back on the raft. We were always afraid a shark would get him.*

This theme of hunger, burning thirst, cool sea water and patrolling sharks was repeated in many wartime stories in the Pacific.

Captain Eddy Rickenbacker, during his epic raft voyage in 1942, also told of cruising sharks and the determination of one of his men on the raft to get rid of the nuisances. He stabbed viciously at one of them with a knife, but all he succeeded in doing was to tear the rubberised canvas. That, naturally, gave them a further headache.

Many survivors claim the sharks at times tried to overturn their rafts. There are many accounts supporting this theory. In one instance a small raft 1.5 metres square supported three men — one later succumbed — for twelve days. Because of the excessive weight the raft had to carry, it floated 8 centimetres below the surface. Sharks continually rubbed along its side, slid underneath and jostled the helpless vessel while the unhappy men just sat quietly praying and waiting for rescue.

There is a story of a small raft, forced to carry ten men for five days. On the first day, two sharks began circling at a distance and on the fourth day they had moved in to within a few metres. By this time four men, sitting huddled together, were the only survivors.

Then the sharks came right in and pushed their snouts over

the side. A Goanese steward was too weak to pull clear one of his legs that was dangling in the water. A shark snapped it off. The monsters then disappeared.

On 1 April 1953 the British freighter *Alendi Hill* docked at Singapore with a Foreign Legion deserter picked up in the Bay of Bengal. Weak and emaciated — he weighed only 25 kilograms — the legionnaire Tiira Ensio, a Finn, had been adrift on a 1.2 metre square raft for thirty-four days.

Ensio told one of the spine-chilling stories which so often come from the sea. The Finn and a companion were on their way to Indo-China in a troopship when they decided to desert. Thinking they were near the coast of Sumatra, they unlashed a raft on the night of 21 February and slid overboard. The winds did not favour them. They missed Sumatra, and were blown into the Bay of Bengal.

Their rations were soon gone but they managed to survive on a turtle, a few crabs and some fish. On the eighteenth day out, Ensio's companion died. He kept the body on the raft with him for a week hoping they would be rescued. Then the sharks came and followed the raft. They struck at it and made terrifying efforts to get at the body. Ensio slid it overboard. Immediately the water became alive with sharks and the attacks on the raft ceased.

Late in March, the midnight watch on *Alendi Hill* heard a shout and saw the raft. As the Finn, now just a mass of skin, bones and saltwater sores, was being hauled on board he slipped back into the water. A shark — the sea was alive with them — immediately shot into the attack but missed. It was unable to turn in time and crashed into the freighter's hull.

Some authorities have suggested that the advent of a rescuing boat or aircraft might perhaps incite a shark to attack a man in the water — and that in a number of cases, men have been taken just as a ship was bearing down on them (Whitley).

An even more macabre story concerns the steamer *Una* which ran aground early one morning in November 1918 on the Muchoir Banks 100 kilometres north of San Domingo in the West Indies. The officers and crew saved themselves in the lifeboats but there were not sufficient lifeboats for 75 labourers, who had to resort to floats. Some of the floats were standard, but others were hastily made out of hatch covers and other loose cargo.

The sea was fairly smooth and in less than an hour the water around the doomed steamer was infested with sharks varying from 2.5 to 5 metres.

Some of the floats were overloaded. They tipped and rocked. Here and there a man fell overboard and the sharks were at him, tearing him to pieces. The killers grew bolder and even attacked the terror-stricken men on the rafts, trying to knock them off with their powerful tails. With their own momentum the sharks got their heads over the edge of the rafts, snatching their prey at random by the arms or legs and dragging them into the sea. Some of the floats tipped to such an angle, when the sharks' heads were pressed on the edge, that the screaming men could hold on no longer and slid into the water. There they were torn to pieces within seconds. Some of the sharks swam under the rafts and tried to lift them out of the water with their backs. They often succeeded, dumping all hands overboard.

The men had no weapons, except a few oars. These soon broke or were torn from their grasp. The tragedy of surviving one disaster only to be thrown into the teeth of an even greater horror sent some men insane and many jumped overboard right into the jaws of their persecutors.

Little information is available about the shark experiences of shipwreck survivors on flotanets and Carley floats. These floats, which were used by naval and merchant ships during the war, were never intended to be more than a temporary means of support and few survivors have lived on them more than a few days.

The Carley float, or "life float", looks like a large, oval lifebelt made of a steel cylinder with a loose rope network only as flooring. The flotanet is a rope net made buoyant by a series of cork floats or buoys.

There is an incident concerning a batch of Carley floats packed with wartime shipwreck survivors. For three and a half days they had kept within hailing distance of each other until, when rescued, they were so weak and delirious they hardly had the strength to shout. For the first day or two there was a good deal of swimming from float to float and the sharks were active. Many of the men disappeared from sight in a mass of churning, bloodstained water.

Dr Macdonald Critchley, who during the war interviewed all

shipwreck survivors on behalf of the British Navy, published the results of his research in a book entitled *Shipwreck Survivors*. He says this of a person's chance of survival on floats and rafts:

> *Both in the case of the flotanet and the Carley float, the survivor is deeply immersed, the craft being either awash or slightly submerged. Until lately, no equipment was carried, or at the most a pair of paddles and a barrel of water. The simplest forms of raft were only a little less adequate, being capable of supporting a few men in a squatting posture, probably submerged several inches, and devoid of life-saving appliances of any kind. The more modern rafts, such as the Chipchase, Cocks', Echans', or the Spoonfos patterns, are very different, for they carry devices directed towards protection from the weather, navigation, and the stowage of water, food and medical requisites.*
>
> *What are the chances of survival under such conditions? No dogmatic answer can be given, but it can be said that the Carley float and the flotanet have kept men alive for as long as three and a half days, despite the rigours of tropical or sub-arctic weather.*
>
> *The longest survival period upon a raft has been, up to date, forty-eight days. The record for a lifeboat voyage has been seventy days, though the chances of making land or being spotted and picked up by aircraft or ships within a much shorter time, are considerable.*
>
> *The hazards of the float survivor do not end there. In tropical and sub-tropical waters sharks are a deadly problem. The story is almost routine—large numbers of sharks following craft and drawing closer as each day passes. Despite heat that can send men crazy, the survivors must sit in the broiling sun for the monsters dominate the water. It is impossible for the ringed men even to dangle their feet in the water. A shark is always ready to thrust in and snap.*

Dr Macdonald Critchley questions whether sharks are as aggressive as usually imagined and whether they will deliberately overturn a raft or boat:

> *Certainly they can often be scared away with an oar or by threshing or splashing around them. A swimmer who churns*

up the water vigorously often evades attack. When sharks do
brush against a boat, it is possible that they are trying to
scratch their backs, or rid themselves of sea lice or passenger
fish (the so-called remoras or shark-suckers).

Survival at sea has always been a subject of lively research
by seafaring nations. During World War II in Great Britain and
the United States the subject was scientifically studied. In the
United States, an organisation known as the Arctic, Desert,
Tropic Information Centre (ADTIC) was established by the US
Air Force to examine this and similar problems. The results of
this research were published in *Airmen against the Sea* by Dr
George Llano. A considerable section of the report was devoted
to experiences with sharks, whales and porpoises.

The likelihood of shark attack, the report stated, is a matter
of real concern to all airmen who fly over water, and there can
no longer be any question that sharks are a grave danger to those
exposed to them. Nevertheless, although concern was often
expressed in the narratives of survivors — especially those from
tropical regions — only twenty-eight out of 2500 odd accounts
examined represented contact — visual or otherwise — with sharks.
In only twelve cases was there any injury. In all cases the men
reported they were able to reach the life rafts before the sharks
appeared. Some sharks appeared within thirty minutes and most
within twenty-four hours. In some cases, the first and only shark
did not show up until the fourth, ninth or thirteenth day. While
in most instances the sharks cruised around the rafts or took
up position beneath them, at other times they appeared to be
attracted by the paddles and attempted to bite them. Other
reports show they bumped up against the raft, often with
sufficient force to lift the raft and its occupants 10 centimetres
or so into the air. This at times caused considerable damage.

Some of the survivors commented that they believed the shark's
interest in the raft was not aroused by its occupants but by the
fish clustered beneath it. One group of survivors said sharks never
left them and became progressively bolder, leaping out of the
water, spraying the occupants with water, or battering the soft
deck fabric with their tails, while "trying to stun the fish under
the raft". Vomiting over the side of the raft also appeared to
attract them. In one instance as many as eight sharks "made
passes at the raft as if to upset it".

The superstition that sharks can sense death appeared in the narratives frequently. Rickenbacker reported that after the death of one of his crew, sharks appeared in greater numbers. A nine-day survivor in the Gulf of Mexico said sharks took the body of his companion from the raft shortly after death. Men were hesitant to commit a body to the sea and sometimes delayed doing so for a day or two. Some feared it would attract sharks and none wished to witness the mauling of the body. For these reasons the report considered that the best time to conduct burials was at night. The report also suggests that "those who hesitated in disposing of the dead endangered their own lives".

Bad as the plight of men in lifeboats and rafts may appear, it is immeasurably better than that of the lone ocean survivors swimming free or in lifebelts. There are occasional stories of men falling overboard in tropical waters and being devoured by sharks, and terrifying tales of the experiences of survivors of shipwreck and aircraft crashes.

When the American freighter *Mormackite*, bound from Buenos Aires to Baltimore, capsized and sank off the coast of Virginia in October 1954, she went down so quickly that she couldn't even send an SOS. Shortly after, the pilot of an aircraft saw fifteen men in lifebelts and dropped rubber rafts. Later the airman reported he saw some bodies in the water which were apparently being attacked by a mob of milling sharks. Survivors told of fighting off sharks and of thoughts of suicide as they clung to floating wreckage and rafts.

The same type of story was told by the survivors of an airliner carrying farm workers from Puerto Rico to the United States, which early in June 1950 crashed into the Atlantic Ocean off the coast of Florida. Fortunately, stories of this kind are uncommon.

It is hard to imagine a more pitiful situation than that of swimmers alone for long periods in a limitless ocean. Yet many persons have successfully survived the ordeal for days and nights, even in the presence of sharks.

Just before Christmas Day 1948, a 13-year-old lad, clad in a lifebelt, was washed ashore on the Cuban coast. He was in a pathetic condition — he had been forty hours in the water — and his story was at first hard to believe.

The lad, Tony Latona, of California, told how he had been playing with another messboy, Bent Jeppsen, 14, on the afterdeck of the Danish ship *Grete Maersk* when Jeppsen fell overboard about 16 kilometres off Cape Maisi, Cuba. Tony threw a lifebelt to Jeppsen, then jumped overboard to help him. Their shouts were not heard, and the ship ploughed on. They had been in the water for two hours when they spotted sharks coming in to the attack. One struck Jeppsen and ripped two great gashes in his left foot. Jeppsen yelled. Latona's story went on:

We kicked and kicked and drove the sharks away. I told Jeppsen that the blood in the water would drive the sharks crazy. I told him to take off his trousers and bind them around his gashed foot to help stop the bleeding. We did not see the sharks then but they must have been hanging around, because an hour later when Jeppsen's trousers fell off, the sharks were back after us in a few minutes. They just swam past me and tried to get at Jeppsen. We kept driving them off but they came back every fifteen minutes. Jeppsen was losing blood and getting weak.

Then a shark struck him on the same foot again. He said it hurt. The sharks kept coming back more often, paying less attention to our efforts to drive them off. Pretty soon one struck Jeppsen under the arm. He cried when it gashed him. Another shark came in and tore his knee. He yelled and started going under.

He went down screaming, "My foot." He came up fighting and screaming, and then went down again. That is the last I saw of him. I saw blood in the water. I sat in the lifebelt and hung my feet over the side and paddled with my hands until I got too tired. When daylight came I was close to land but all day currents drifted me away. Next night the sharks returned, one striking at me and tearing the seat of my trousers. On the morning of the second day a current carried me towards a coral reef and I waded ashore.

The story of Edward Sierks also illustrates what grit and determination can at times accomplish in an apparently hopeless situation. Sierks, a 40-year-old yachtsman, fell from his yacht, *L'Apache*, in July 1951. He was skippering *L'Apache* in the 3580 kilometre Los Angeles–Honolulu yacht race when he suddenly went overboard. He was kept afloat by a lifebuoy which had been tossed over the side. Thirty hours later, the US destroyer

Douglas A. Munro pulled the exhausted yachtsman from the water. He told of being molested by a 2 metre shark which nibbled his bare feet until his knife left the creature lifeless in the sea.

Other survivors have endured incredible hardships. A terrible story of a man's two-hour fight for life against sharks and predatory birds in the pitch blackness of a tropical sea was told by the crew of the SS *Ripley Castle* when she berthed in July 1926.

Just south of the Equator, between Philadelphia and Cape Town, Tony Madison, a 26-year-old seaman, lost his balance and fell into the water. His fall was unobserved and he was not missed for an hour. The captain immediately put the ship about and near 2 a.m. faint cries were heard. Two buoys with flares were tossed overboard and Madison was seen struggling in the water. When he was pulled aboard both legs were bleeding from shark injuries and his face was torn and pecked by great birds which had swarmed down on him.

Not all men swimming in the sea or floating in life jackets are attacked, although sharks may cruise quite close. During the war it was reported that often the creatures did not react as expected and in many instances, men swam long distances in shark-infested waters unmolested.

Sharks are known to be inquisitive and reference has already been made to their bumping tactics. They will investigate any large floating object. After investigation the shark will usually swim away. But at other times it may approach or circle the object in the water and bump or nudge it. Lifebelt swimmers are at times molested in this way without coming to much harm.

This happened to the captain of an aircraft which was forced to land in the sea some kilometres offshore from Lae in New Guinea. During his shoreward swim a shark bumped into his side, but made no further assault.

But Lieutenant-Commander Kabat found that sharks can be more persistent. He was an officer of the US Destroyer *Duncan* which was sunk off Guadalcanal in October 1942. Wounded were placed on the only two life rafts on the ship — the others had been put overboard to help the survivors of an aircraft carrier two days before. The rest of the crew were in life jackets. Kabat, in a kapok life jacket, was one of those who spent most of the night in the water. For buoyancy he used two aluminium powder tins. Soon after dawn he felt a scratching, tickling sensation on his left foot and found it was bleeding. He then noticed less than 3 metres away the glistening brown back of a 1.5 metre shark.

It swam around and then attacked again. Kabat tried to force the shark off with his fist. After the shark swam away, he noticed a piece of flesh had been torn from his left hand. At intervals of about fifteen minutes he was attacked several times. On each occasion he received some injury, so that his big toe was dangling, a piece of his right heel was gone and his left elbow, hand and calf were torn. Kabat said after: "If he did not actually sink his teeth into me, his rough hide would scrape off great pieces of my skin."

In further attacks, his thigh was so deeply gashed that the bone was exposed. The unfortunate man was rescued by a destroyer. Later he recovered.

No account of the experiences of lone swimmers with sharks would be complete without further reference to the valuable contributions on this subject of Dr George Llano and his studies of the narratives of US airmen who, during the war, had either bailed out or ditched at sea, and whose only refuge for days on end was a life raft or the tenuous support of a Mae West life jacket. The narratives revealed that the men had often spent long periods in the water amid sharks without being molested and that some of the escapes seemed little short of miraculous.

Dr Llano tells of a navy ensign parachuted into the water off Cape Engano, Palau Islands, near north-east Luzon in the Philippines (lat. 18°35′N) who spent eight hours in shark-infested waters. He lost his life raft when the parachute opened and damaged his life jacket. As he swam, his socks gradually worked off.

He was joined by four sharks about 1.2 to 1.5 metres long which did not seem to bother him while he kicked. As soon as he stopped, he said, one of them would "make a pass" at him. In this manner one of the sharks grazed his legs.

Dr Llano suggests that although clothing cannot be depended upon to prevent attacks by sharks on persons in life jackets, the sharks are more apt to bite a bare body. He quotes examples to support his statement.

During the war the engine of an S2N failed 110 kilometres

east of Wallis Island in the Central Pacific (lat. 12°S), 400 kilometres west of Samoa. The plane had to be ditched. In the impact the pilot, Lieutenant A. G. Reading, was knocked unconscious. He was rescued by his radioman, ARMCE Almond, who pulled him out of the cockpit and inflated his life jacket. Reading soon recovered consciousness. The men pulled their dye-markers and tied themselves together with the cords but soon drifted away from the dye. Reading was clothed, but Almond was wearing only shorts, with his legs bare. After about half an hour, sharks appeared. Soon afterwards Almond said something had struck his right foot. His foot was bleeding and he tried to hold it out of the water. Then the sharks struck again and both men were dragged under for a moment. The water around them was stained with blood. There were five sharks altogether. Not only did Almond's right leg have numerous wounds, but his left thigh was also badly lacerated. He felt no great pain, although the sharks continued to strike at him.

A white shark with its nose back and its teeth lowered, ready to attack. RON TAYLOR

Reading hit at the passing sharks with his binoculars, but almost immediately the brutes again struck at Almond. Both men went under together and when they surfaced, Reading found he was separated from Almond. Then he received a sharp whack on his cheekbone from the flying tail of one of the sharks. This shark continued to attack Almond, now under-water. The sharks kept circling and every now and then Reading could feel one with his foot. He was rescued at midnight after sixteen hours in the water.

Another example quoted by Dr Llano supports the view of many skindivers and others interested in these matters, that men grouped together, especially if clothed, are safer than a lone swimmer. The longest period of survival in shark-infested waters involved a group of men who spent forty-two hours together in the water. Eight of the twelve who survived the ditching were fully clothed, although some removed or lost their shoes after entering the water.

They lashed themselves together and hung on to a salvaged wing float. One man soon died and about this time the sharks appeared. The men tried to drive them away by shooting at them and kicking. The men were not particularly bothered by the sharks during darkness. At daybreak one man, reported to have been bitten slightly, became frightened and died during the second night. Two others became delirious and died. The remaining men were rescued by a passing merchantman at 5 a.m. the following day.

Sir John Smythe, VC, in the House of Commons recently told a somewhat similar story about the sinking of the British cruisers *Dorsetshire* and *Cornwall* by dive-bombers in the Indian Ocean in 1942.

Captain A. W. Shelton Agar, VC, of the *Dorsetshire* realised that greater danger to hundreds of men in the water came from sharks than from dive-bombers.

Captain Agar and those still alive decided the only way to keep the sharks off was to bring all the dead bodies to the centre and make a circle of live men around them. They remained this way in the water for thirty-six hours fighting off sharks with sixty corpses in their midst.

Although the horror of some of the attacks described in this chapter is magnified by the scale of the carnage, sharks are an equal danger to survivors of accidents to smaller boats. In recent years two gruesome attacks in coastal waters of Queensland have reminded Australians of this.

Moreton Bay is an aquatic playground, fishing, boating and sailing area for the growing capital of Queensland, Brisbane. It would be impossible to calculate how many times Vic Beaver had gone down the Bay for the weekend to relax and fish. At 74 he could clearly remember his visit to Lady Musgrave Island at the time of Zane Grey's expedition to the island, and his achievement in landing a 62 kilogram sailfish, which was the biggest weighed in Australia for some forty years. Vic Beaver was accompanied by Verdon Harrison, aged 33, and John Hayes, aged 40. They were crossing the Bay on Friday night, 11 March 1977, as they had countless times, when through the rain, Harrison saw a 25,000 tonne freighter on a collision course. The collision took place, their launch sank, and all they could salvage was a one-metre icebox and a rubber mattress. The three men drifted clinging to the icebox for some thirty-six hours, and on at least two occasions saw other craft but could not attract their attention. They were menaced for some time by small sharks and then the small sharks were joined by a big one.

This shark attacked and afterwards came back two or three times. When it attacked Vic Beaver, Harrison tried to hold Beaver and to discourage the shark by kicking and punching, but he had no success. He recalled later:

I tried to hold Vic with me as he was pulled off the edge of the box. Vic just said, "It's got me again. Goodbye mates, this is it," and then he was gone. That's all he said as it took him. John and I tried to squeeze inside the icebox, but we could only get our heads and shoulders inside and the shark still kept going under us. I punched and kicked at the shark and cut myself a bit, then the shark circled again and John screamed, "It's got my foot!" He told me to keep in the box and then the shark took him. I tried to climb into the icebox for safety, but this big bastard tried to climb in with me.

Forty-five minutes after the attack, Verdon Harrison was rescued by the crew of another fishing boat. The big shark could have been either a white or a tiger, both of which are in the Bay.

A second incident, in North Queensland, also resulted in the deaths of two people out of a group of three.

Ray Boundy was the skipper of a 14 metre prawn trawler,

trawling near the reefs out from Townsville. One of the booms for the trawl net broke, and whilst it was being secured, a big wave heeled the boat, causing it to capsize. Boundy, his crew-man Dennis Murphy, aged 24, and Linda Horton of Townsville, aged 21, sat on top of the upturned hull to decide what to do. Their decision was to leave the sinking boat and to use a surfboard, a life ring and pieces of foam from the wreckage to head towards two other reefs, Lodestone and Keeper, where other trawlers were working.

Between one o'clock on Monday morning 25 July 1983 and sunset on Monday night, they were within 8 kilometres of Lodestone. They saw search aircraft, but the aircraft did not spot them in the 2 or 3 metre swell.

Soon after dark a shark started following them, pushing at pieces of foam, the life ring and the surfboard. "We weren't taking much notice of him," Boundy later recalled, "thinking if we didn't antagonise him he would leave us alone." The shark was interested in Boundy's leg, but he kicked it with his other foot and the shark let go and disappeared.

Ten minutes later, a big wave rolled the three from their floats into the water, and the trouble started again. "Next thing my mate [Murphy] was screaming his head off, he said, 'He's got my leg, the bastard's got my leg.'" Murphy then said, "Well it looks like that's it, you and Lindy bolt," and swam four strokes in the direction of the shark. "We heard a lot of screaming and kicking and punching," Boundy said, "and then saw the shark hit his body upside down out of the water and eat it."

Everything seemed to be all right for a couple of hours, according to Boundy, but the shark turned up again about 4 a.m.

> Lindy was sitting in the sling of the lifebuoy with her feet up on the foam. I was pretty sure he was the same shark. This time he came along as slow as you like beside, then grabbed Lindy around the arms and the chest while she was still in the life preserver, [and] shook her about three or four times causing the life ring to fall off. She only let out one little squeal as soon as it hit and I knew almost instantly that she was dead.

Boundy used two pieces of foam to paddle away, and just after daylight the shark came back again and circled him. "I thought I'd never get out of it because he just kept circling closer and closer, then I saw the reef, and knew that if I made it there and jumped the outer reef, he wouldn't come there after me." Boundy surfed over the edge of the reef to safety with a small piece of foam. The search aircraft spotted him at this time and he was picked up and lifted to safety by an RAAF helicopter. The attacker or attackers in this incident were probably tiger sharks or big whalers, both common in the area.

MEETING THE MENACE

Like most other problems, those of protection and defence against shark attack have a number of different aspects. First there is the problem of protection against sharks in the open seas. This is largely the concern of navies, air forces, mercantile marine and airlines. Then there are the problems with which this book is largely concerned of swimmers and others in coastal waters. This is mainly the concern of national, governmental, municipal and civic bodies and of swimming and surfing clubs and associations. Skindivers and spearfishermen have other problems. Common to all is the problem of individual and personal protection.

In other pages of this book advice is given on the precautions individuals should take. Opinions differ about the value of repellents. Japan is the only place where individual swimmers take steps for their protection. They swim wearing a long sash known as a *fundoshi* trailing from a belt behind them.

At many beaches, especially in Australia, considerable value is placed on the use of lookout towers and warning bells. Bathers on most Australian beaches bathe between "safe" flags. As soon as the lookout sights a shark, a bell is rung. Bathers rapidly leave the water until the shark disappears or is chased out to sea by boats or surf skis. Air patrols also operate frequently over the more popular beaches during the summer months.

Numerous methods have been devised for protecting swimmers, skindivers and survivors of shipwrecks and air crashes against roaming man-eaters. Many have been tried in the Sydney area. These methods had one thing in common — they were usually complicated.

The more expensive methods mostly involve barriers of some kind. Usually these require governmental or municipal assistance. There has been much debate about various methods and materials, enclosures versus nets, whether the nets should be fixed or mobile, whether they should be made of rope, nylon, steel rings or aluminium. But no form of fixed mechanical barrier has ever proved effective for long in the presence of wave action.

The idea that surfers could be protected by a netted enclosure was first put into practical effect at Durban, South Africa, when a safety bathing enclosure was erected in 1907. The net was repeatedly smashed by heavy seas. It was constantly undergoing repair at heavy cost. Eventually, the sea won and in 1928 people were complaining it was an eyesore. By 1933 very little of the original structure remained. The only parts visible were a number of the piles with a few remnants of the netting suspended from cables.

A netting enclosure erected at Coogee, New South Wales, in 1929 went the same way as the Durban 1907 project and was finally abandoned. It needed frequent and costly repairs, and often large holes — big enough for most sharks — appeared in the net.

Even if someone devised a net which would remain intact without prohibitive maintenance costs, the shark problem would not be entirely solved. No net that will last without continuous maintenance has yet been made. They all succumb to the battering of the seas, abrasion, and destruction by marine growth. Oysters and similar shellfish encrust the nets enthusiastically and quickly destroy them. Channels also form beneath the nets. Even if sharks cannot swim under a net or through holes in it, they can often swim over it with the utmost ease. The centre of a net always sags and is often well below water level at spring and other high tides.

All these facts are also true of nets and other enclosures in harbours and less troubled ocean waters where rusting, abrasion and destruction by marine growth vanquish them just as quickly. Keeping a net shark-proof for any length of time appears to be humanly impossible. On many occasions, sharks, usually small ones, have actually been found inside enclosures. A young spearfisherman saw a 1.2 metre shark in the Manly Harbour pool. The shark, which was caught, proved to be a harmless wobbegong, but the diver said a 1.8 metre shark was also there.

The Sydney *Sun* newspaper sent a reporter on an underwater examination of the nets around the baths in the Sydney area. He claimed to have found at least six unsafe, with holes big enough to admit large sharks. A 2 metre specimen was found in the "shark-proof" pool at Sandgate and an even larger shark has been found in a netted enclosure in the Parramatta River. There have been similar reports from Queensland where the inevitable happened and a bather was attacked and killed by a shark in a "shark-proof" enclosure.

Electrical fishing is in its infancy, but the time may come when laneways or barriers of electrically-charged water will either kill fish or drive them into nets. Electrical devices to stun sharks might be satisfactory in still water, but there are many drawbacks to its use on beaches, with no guarantee of effectiveness.

According to Mr T. C. Roughley, a Sydney fisheries expert, an electric current stopped a shark during an experiment at Port Hacking. A 3.5 metre shark swam towards an electric barrier and stopped as if paralysed. It remained as stiff as a ramrod while the electric current was on, but when the current was stopped it swam lazily away, as if nothing had happened.

The Sutherland Shire Council once investigated the possibilities of erecting an electric barrier at South Cronulla, but dropped the plan because of prohibitive cost. The Manly Council also considered erecting anti-shark electrified wires along the ocean beach. It did not go on with the scheme, as it thought bathers would not like the idea of swimming near electrified wires, and that the electricity might scare off more bathers than sharks.

South Africans have been active in experimenting with electricity as a shark repellent or deterrent. Dr E. D. Smith from the National Physics Research Laboratory developed an eddy current electrode system. This has appeared to be successful with some shark species which are reluctant to cross the barrier. However, as with other deterrents, the effectiveness could vary among species.

In one series of experiments a lemon shark turned instantly away from the electric field; on the other hand a tiger shark apparently found the field attractive and turned towards it, breaking the electrode in the process.

Research is continuing into various forms of chemical repellent even though the American shark chaser and its British equivalent have now been withdrawn because of their ineffectiveness on some species and in some circumstances. Dr Johnson, working from the Undersea Centre at San Diego, developed this device which is now often called "a floating shark screen" or "survival sack". The screen is a bigger-than-man-size plastic bag and is supported on the surface by the three inflatable collars. One, two or three of these collars are inflated, then the user climbs into the bag and fills it with water so it hangs as a dark uninteresting shape under the surface. Sharks seem to be reluctant to approach this dark plastic shape, even though the inflatable rings are coloured safety yellow, for maximum surface visibility. This floating screen is very effective in emergencies. Any blood or other potential shark attractant materials are retained in the bag. The shark screen folds into a small pack and is easily carried in emergency equipment.

John Hicks of Florida, USA, built a compact underwater electronic shark repellent. This repellent had long antennae and emitted electronic impulses which appeared to cause sharks to shy away when they came within range. This device was extensively tested by the United States Armed Services and NASA, but apparently, once again, the unpredictable behaviour of the giant predator made the device less effective in some circumstances. One advantage of electric and electronic repellents is that they repel through 360° rather than just down current as in chemical repellents or directional repellents that have to be fired.

The "shark chaser" mixture of copper acetate and other chemicals is also effective in some cases, but as in other repellents, different species react in different ways and add to the overall dangerous conditions.

The theory of the repellent's action was based on claims that sharks will not eat dead sharks, that hungry ones will turn tail when they come into the vicinity of a dead and decomposing shark and that they will not touch putrefying shark flesh as bait. Experiments were carried out to determine the essential chemical element which deterred the sharks, and a formula was produced whose main ingredient was copper acetate. The American Cyanamide Company undertook the production of thousands of the repellent units, which were issued to all US Navy fliers in the Pacific.

The copper acetate was mixed with other chemicals to delay its solution and a deep blue dye was added to colour the water around the swimmer. All these ingredients, packed inside a thin bag, were put into a special waterproof packet and placed in a pocket inside the life jacket. Crashed airmen had merely to pull a tag to release the repellent. The water surrounding the swimmer immediately became deep blue. The action of the repellent lasted for about six hours.

After the war, repellents were immediately and widely adopted. Lifesaving clubs tied the chemicals to buoys at surf carnivals. They were trailed in bags behind surf boats, tied to surf skis and surfboards, hung from swimmers' necks and dangled from rescue belts. Fishermen used the repellents to protect their nets.

For a time it was thought the repellent was going to be the complete answer to the problem of protection from sharks, unsolvable since the days of ancient sponge divers. Then the novelty passed. Reports of its value have been conflicting, and people have begun to wonder how really effective these chemicals are. But research is continuing.

The Mote Marine Laboratory at Cape Haze, under the leadership of Dr Perry Gilbert, is the centre of much of the world's shark research. Dr Eugenie Clark of this institution has been investigating the possibilities of a repellent based on the natural poison exuded from the skin of the Red Sea moses sole (*Pardachirus marmoratus*). The repellent substance is called pardaxin. Some of the characteristics of pardaxin are similar to those of industrial detergents, so perhaps this flatfish may give the lead to the laboratory preparation of a similar repellent. Experiments with industrial detergents sprayed at sharks clearly indicate repellent effects.

Use of the US Navy floating shark screen, a one-person blow-up all-encompassing emergency envelope, would no doubt have prevented at least some of the horrific loss of life in the past, and especially in World War II, from ship sinkings and aircraft ditchings, described elsewhere in this book.

Another school of thought considers that shark destruction offers the best method of protection, and many methods have been suggested. While some authorities are in favour of shooting sharks, it is generally felt there might be more casualties among the bathers than among the sharks. Shooting has not received much support, although, as mentioned later, the whaling station men think a lot of this method. Chasing the sharks with sticks of gelignite tied to a brick, dynamite, and depth charges have also been suggested.

Not only does the explosion affect the shark at which it is aimed, but it will kill or stun every fish in the immediate vicinity. The experience of those who have used explosives to get an easy supply of fish was that this method, instead of killing all the sharks in the vicinity, merely flattened strays close to the explosion and attracted others, which came in mobs, to gorge themselves on the ready-made meal of stunned and dead fishes.

In his book *Shark*, Commander F. D. Fane, USNR, gives a detailed description of the reaction of sharks to the explosion of half-kilogram blocks of TNT. Commander Fane says:

> *Large numbers of fish were killed or stunned by the explosion and lay on the bottom or drifted on the surface. Within twenty seconds, sharks came into the area from all directions. They struck at the injured fish, some of which were large snappers and bass running from 10 to 30 lb [4.5 to 13.5 kilograms], devouring them head first. If a part of a fish protruded from the jaws of one shark, it was struck at by the other sharks.*
>
> *By observations through a water glass it was noted that the shark reaction to explosion was to spin about and speed away at the moment of detonation, only to return within ten to twenty seconds. Repeated blasts did not keep them away.*
>
> *The sharks were able to navigate at high speed in the thick soapy fog caused by the explosives and over the irregular bottom through coral pinnacles.*

Some years ago, when scientists from the American Museum went live-specimen hunting at Penrhyn they evolved a novel method of stunning fishes with dynamite. They called the contraption a "bang-bang". The men fixed a couple of dynamite caps to a 3 metre pole and when the fish they were after was close enough the switch was closed. This stunned the fish without killing it.

But there is always great danger to those who handle explosives while searching for sharks. In July 1956, two men were killed and two were critically injured off the English coast while naval personnel were preparing for diving operations. Four men in a dinghy saw a shark and tried to scare it off by throwing in a line with two 400 gram charges of explosive attached. The line tangled around the shark. It then made for the dinghy and the explosive went off just as it was directly below the frail craft.

Shark fishing from beaches with set lines or traps is also roundly condemned by some shark authorities on the grounds that because it relies for success on some form of lure, it encourages sharks to beaches in search of food. The authorities say sharks have an acute sense of smell and add that the berleying of sharks and the habit of fishermen of leaving bait and other scraps to be swept back into the water by the tide creates a source of danger. Many shark authorities believe also that dumping of rubbish at sea off beaches creates the same danger. Dumping of rubbish should, they claim, be prohibited closer in than 11 kilometres.

Bubbles have also been suggested as a means of warding off prowling sharks and a bathing area has been envisaged which is surrounded by pipes emitting a continuous stream of air, carbon dioxide and other gases.

The bubble advocates pointed to the immunity from attack of the dress diver, which they attributed to the continuous stream of bubbles flowing from the helmet. They also claimed the dress diver could scare sharks with a stream of bubbles aimed at them from the sleeve of the diving suit.

Dr Perry Gilbert, however, has shown by extensive experiments that bubble barriers are ineffective.

Queensland, Australia's warm tropical water state, had suffered twenty-seven fatalities between 1914 and 1984. Meshing and drum set lines were introduced as anti-shark measures in 1962. Since then, Queensland has had only one fatality. These measures were first taken on popular Brisbane north and South Coast beaches and Cairns.

In 1963 the measures were extended to Mackay and Townsville, and to Rockhampton in 1968, Point Lookout in 1973, and Bundaberg and Rainbow Beach in 1974. In some areas, for ecological reasons, set lines are used without the support of mesh nets. In 1984, 47 nets and 189 drum set lines were used. The set lines took 18.3 per cent of the total catch.

The Queensland combination of set lines and mesh nets, despite some concern about the baits attracting sharks, has been

White sharks, as well as other species, are regularly trapped in net meshes.
RON AND VALERIE TAYLOR

successful. The Queensland nets are 200 metres long and 6.4 metres in depth. They are set about 500 metres from shore. The nets do not set down to the sea bed. As in other areas where meshing has been introduced, the Queensland statistics show the greatest number of sharks taken in the initial years of operation. In this state, however, perhaps because of its warm tropical water, the decline in the catch over the years has not been as marked as off the Sydney beaches. It is interesting to note that among New South Wales meshed beaches, the most northern meshed area, Newcastle, also maintains a much higher catch rate than beaches off Sydney and further south off Wollongong. In Queensland, the take of tiger/whaler and, in the south, white sharks has been remarkably steady.

The main anti-shark measure used off surfing beaches in New South Wales, as in South Africa, is the mesh net. In New South Wales, meshing was introduced as an anti-shark measure in January 1935. It was extended in 1937 and again in 1949 to cover the most popular surfing beaches. Clearly, any effective anti-shark measure reduces the shark population in a particular area,

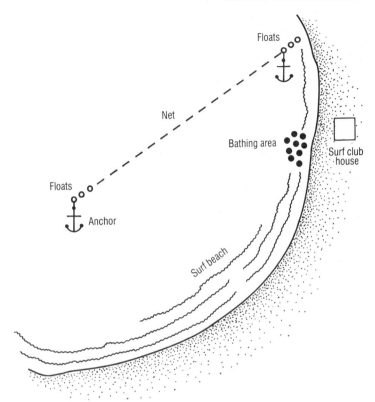

Meshing. Position of nets in relation to a beach.

and so reduces the likelihood of attack. Off Sydney, where meshing was first introduced, there has been only one attack, a non-fatal attack off Bondi. There has, however, been one fatality off Newcastle, a meshed area, in 1951.

Since the introduction of meshing at Durban in 1952, there were only three attacks until 1978 — all non-fatal attacks in the Durban area. Dunedin, New Zealand, following a series of attacks, also introduced meshing, and again its effectiveness has been shown.

Before meshing was introduced, however, shark attacks off Sydney beaches were becoming so frequent that there was a pronounced public lack of confidence in bathing, and in 1934 the New South Wales Government set up a special Shark Menace

Advisory Committee to investigate and report on the best methods of protecting bathers from the man-killers.

A surfing authority, Mr Adrian Curlewis, later Judge Sir Adrian Curlewis, was created chairman. When the committee finally brought down its report the main recommendation was that the Government should subsidise systematic and continuous meshing along the metropolitan coastline to Port Hacking. Many proclaimed that meshing was worthless. But the Government showed wisdom in adopting the report. From the day the first net was set in 1936, although there have been two non-fatal attacks at Merewether, south of Newcastle, there has not been a single shark fatality on a meshed ocean beach near Sydney.

Briefly, meshing consists of a twine or rope net set overnight and removed by a trawler in the morning. Originally 300 metre nets were used in New South Wales, but these were later replaced by 150 metre nets. The number and species of the sharks taken in the mesh nets in New South Wales vary from year to year. In 1976/77 there was a total of 317 sharks netted, and in 1979/80, 325. However, the total for other years have been much lower — 159 in 1977/78, 233 in 1978/79 and 163 in 1980/81. Study of New South Wales shark take by month in the mesh nets shows the increase in shark take from the nets of the potentially dangerous species in the warm summer months. This again reflects that more sharks are present when the ocean water temperature is higher in summer than it is in winter.

The 150 metre nets are laid in pairs. A 14 kilogram anchor

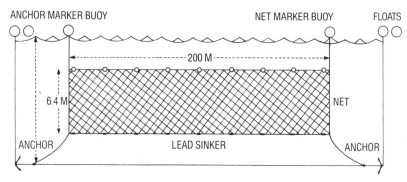

A typical shark mesh net as used on surfing beaches. Sharks can swim under, over or round the sides of the net, yet many are entangled in it.

is thrown over with three glass floats as markers. The net is set as the boat moves at about 6 knots. At the other end another anchor and markers hold the net in position. The floats hold it upright. It is like a long fence parallel to the beach and laid in the position indicated by local knowledge and currents. The mesh is about 30 centimetres square, and if the shark hits the loosely hanging net it becomes entangled. The more it struggles the more tangled it gets.

The practice stopped in 1943 when the United States Armed Forces took over the vessels, but was resumed in 1946.

Without meshing — assuming the previous rate of attacks on the Sydney beaches had been maintained — there would have been about fourteen attacks on these beaches between 1937 and 1956. Actually there were none. First indication of the results of meshing was a sharp reduction in the number of shark alarms in beaches to about one-tenth of those in the years before 1938. Cost of meshing was originally $40,000 for a two-year scheme. It works out that each shark caught costs $28.

Between October 1937 and February 1939, 1500 sharks were meshed between Palm Beach and Cronulla. Of these 900 were large sharks believed to be man-killers. The most noticeable feature of meshing is the reduction in the number of sharks caught each year. For instance, during less than two months, from 28 October 1937 to 19 December 1937, the total number of meshings was 180 and the number of sharks caught was 315. Included in this group were quite a few dangerous sharks — 20 tigers, 8 whalers, 3 blue pointers — in addition to 58 grey nurses and 68 hammerheads.

The whole catch for the twelve months in 1940 was 751 sharks and the tally for fifteen months from July 1953 to October 1954 was 214. Even fewer sharks are now being caught. They are being scared off and their numbers reduced in other ways. Sometimes it's a matter of "killing many birds with the one stone", for sharks are often caught with litters of young inside them.

The number of sharks caught varies on different beaches. In one year — 1937-38 — potentially dangerous sharks caught averaged 40 per beach on the north side of the harbour and 30 on the southern beaches. The largest number was caught at Palm Beach where, strangely, there has never been a shark attack.

Australian east coast beaches now have lines of defence in

Peter Goadby standing alongside a 517 kg female white shark, and standing on the body of another weighing 363 kg. The compact form of the female can be clearly seen. These two were part of a pack of Cape Moreton white sharks that were circling the boat. BOB MILLAR

the ocean currents offshore. Longline and other professional fishermen also help to reduce the shark population. Game-fishing cruisers that go to sea each weekend also contribute to the annual toll. Many of their catches are of species known to be attackers of humans off beaches and in estuaries.

The benefits of regular or permanent meshing off surfing beaches arises from the reduction of the overall number of potentially dangerous species in the shark population, particularly of the resident sharks that are hunting and feeding along the beaches and around the rocky headlands.

Of the sharks considered as potentially dangerous to humans, each year hammerheads of various species make up the greatest proportion of the sharks taken in the nets. Many more of the three proven most dangerous species — white pointers, tigers and whalers — are taken from the meshed Newcastle beaches than from the meshed Sydney metropolitan or Wollongong beaches. Statistics show a high of 22 and a low of 4 white pointers in any year from Newcastle meshed beaches. The Newcastle catches are also greater than those in the Sydney area for the dangerous tiger sharks and Carcharhinid (whaler) species taken off the beaches.

Statistics show a dramatic decrease in the number of dangerous species taken off the Sydney metropolitan beaches. In 1976-77, 20 of the big three — whites, tigers and whalers — were meshed. In 1977-78, it dropped to 7, in 1978-79 to 12, 1979-80 to 23, and in 1980-81 to 14.

There is a theory that sharks are more likely to attack humans when there is a shortage of their natural food. This implies that the dangers of shark attack in any area are intensified when the number of sharks increases beyond the capacity of the supply of food or when the food supply is reduced by excessive fishing or other means.

On the other hand, the risk of attack is lessened by reducing the number of sharks or by an increase in the food supply such as occurs when great shoals of fish pass along the coast.

This theory might also help to explain the variation in sharks' behaviour in relation to attacks at different times of the year and in different latitudes, as well as the apparent freedom from attack of certain areas such as the New South Wales south coast below Port Hacking. Some experts believe there are other

Bob and Dolly Dyer with a day's catch of Queensland Cape Moreton white and tiger sharks. It was not unusual to have numerous white, tiger and whaler sharks circling the boat at the same time. TELEGRAPH NEWSPAPER CO LTD

TOP: *Shark meshing — a large shark netted on a Sydney beach being drawn up in a net onto Gorshenin's meshing boat, Sydney.*

BOTTOM: *Swimming in nets in the annual race from Magnetic Island to Townsville.*

explanations of the success of meshing. One is that the nets swaying in the water are sufficient to scare off the sharks.

In areas where there is bathing and no meshing, special vigilance must be exercised to recognise the presence of a rogue shark. Special precautions must be taken if a shark appears which exhibits signs of ferocity by attacking dogs, tearing nets, taking fish from lines, or cruising about in an obvious and truculent manner.

Once detected, the most determined efforts should be made to destroy such a shark. Bathing in the open should be prohibited, the area should be meshed, baits should be set and by angling and every other means, steps should be taken to rid the area of the menace.

While there have been isolated attacks near meshed beaches the success of meshing is undoubted. The future of repellents, chemical, electric, electronic and acoustic is largely unknown. The use of helicopters during the peak summer season is also helpful in spotting sharks along popular New South Wales and Queensland surfing beaches. Spotting sharks in the surf helps keep humans and sharks apart as often as possible. The quest for repellents is expensive, frustrating and disconcerting, but one day we will find the solution to living in the sea without danger from our great natural predator, the shark.

Until that day comes, however, it is comforting to be able to record that victims of shark attack now have a far greater chance of survival than formerly. This is because we have now learnt a great deal about first-aid and treatment of shark bite.

Reference is made elsewhere to the remarkably successful first-aid and other methods used in Natal. These involve using plasma, blood and other necessary items for treatment, minimising shock, and controlling bleeding at the pressure points instead of dramatically attempting to rush the patient to plasma and necessary medical facilities.

Study and adoption of the South African recommendation and use of the Feinberg Kit would undoubtedly be of benefit in all countries where shark attack is possible, and this area has proved to extend from the Adriatic Sea in the north to the South Island of New Zealand, and to include fresh and brackish as well as salt water.

The key principles in the successful treatment of shark attack victims in South Africa are (a) Stop the bleeding immediately, and (b) Prevent the onset of shock by appropriate treatment.

Once the bleeding has been stopped,
1. *Reassure and comfort the victim, who should have been placed on a towel or blanket.*
2. *Do not move the victim; allow him or her to stabilise.*
3. *Do not give the victim anything to eat or drink, including alcohol.*
4. *Protect the victim from direct sun to avoid overheating. Temperature must be kept as normal as possible.*
5. *Control the crowd to minimise noise, drama and interference.*

Dr Gilbert estimated that each year round the world there are 25 to 30 fatalities, and around 100 attacks.

After many years of research in French Polynesian waters, Dr Nelson of the US Department of the Navy (Office Naval Research) and R. H. Johnson supported the 1963–64 analysis of Dr Baldridge that half to three-quarters of the attacks on humans were "non-feeding aggressive attacks" in which the victim suffered single slash wounds but did not lose a great deal of flesh.

The single slash-type wound closely resembles the marks and cuts found on the bodies of many sharks. There is a possibility that the single slash attacks occur when the shark is attacking and damaging another animal in its environment in the same way that it would slash at another shark.

Increased knowledge of sharks and their habits and the decreasing numbers of potential human attackers in the seas does not lessen the repugnance and fear of humans at the thought of being eaten, and the economic loss to the area or resort where the attack took place. The thought of the possibility of attack has indirectly saved many lives on patrolled swimming beaches because people tend to surf and swim in the areas under surveillance marked as having the least danger from current rips and dangerous breaks.

Understanding and knowledge of the type of attack, whether a bumping or warning, a single slash non-feeding attack, a feeding attack or feeding frenzy is of no help to victims or their friends and relatives. Knowledge and understanding can assist, however, in the development and testing of anti-shark attack repellents and devices, and even improve meshing, all of which will make a hostile environment, that strange underwater ecosystem, safer for humans.

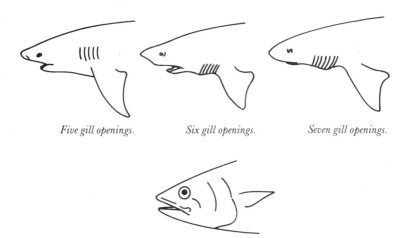

Five gill openings.   *Six gill openings.*   *Seven gill openings.*

The bony fishes have only one gill opening on each side.

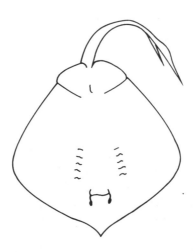

IDENTIFYING FEATURES
OF VARIOUS SPECIES

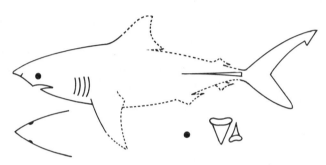

WHITE SHARK:
Bullet nose, black eyes, tail lobes almost equal, well-defined keels on body at tail. No nictitating membrane.
COLOUR — dark grey, light grey or gold above, white under.
TEETH — broad triangular serrated upper jaw, narrow serrated triangular lower jaw.
GILL SLITS — long.

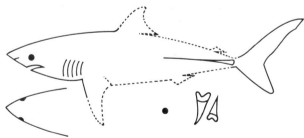

MAKO:
Bullet nose, black eyes, tail lobes almost equal, well-defined keels on body at tail. No nictitating membrane.
COLOUR — blue above, white below.
TEETH — long curved and narrow in both jaws.
GILL SLITS — long.

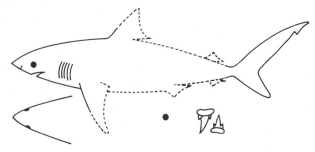

PORBEAGLE:
Bullet nose, black eyes, tail lobes almost equal, well-defined keels on body at tail. No nictitating membrane.
COLOUR — bluish grey above, white below.
TEETH — curved and narrow with cusps on base teeth in both jaws.
GILL SLITS — long.

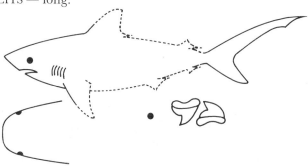

TIGER:
Blunt almost square nose, large dark eyes, upper lobes of tail much longer than low. Small keels on body at tail. No nictitating membrane.
COLOUR — greyish barred and striped above, white below. Colour bars most definite in young and open water sharks.
TEETH — serrated and cockscomb shape, both jaws.

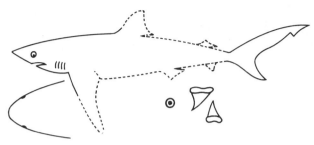

BLUE SHARK:
Pointed head, large dark eye rimmed with white. Upper lobe of tail much longer than lower. Pectoral fin equal to head length to back of gills. Nictitating membrane present.
COLOUR — blue above, white below.
TEETH — broad and serrated upper jaw, narrow serrated lower jaw.
GILL SLITS — short.

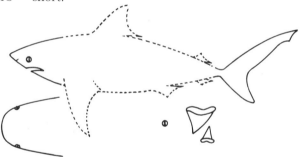

CARCHARINIDS:
(Bull shark and dusky types; leucas, amboinensis, obscurus, galapagensis, plumbeus, altimus, perezi.)
Blunt, rounded head, eyes, yellowish, small pupil. Nictitating membrane. Tail, upper lobe much longer than lower.
COLOUR — dark grey above, white below.
TEETH — finely serrated wide upper jaw, narrow and finely serrated lower jaw.
GILL SLITS — short.

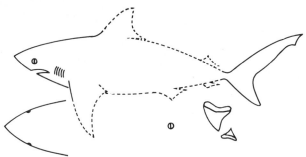

CARCHARINIDS:
(Copper types, brachyurus, falciformis.)
Sharply rounded head, eyes, yellowish, small pupil. Nictitating membrane present. Tail, upper lobe much longer than lower.
COLOUR — copper bronze brown above, white below.
TEETH — finely serrated wide upper jaw, narrow and finely serrated lower jaw.
GILL SLITS — short.

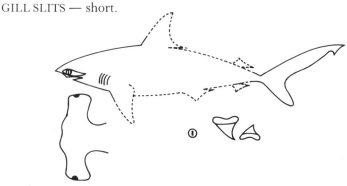

HAMMERHEAD SHARKS, BONNETHEAD SHARKS:
Flattened head extending at right angles to body.

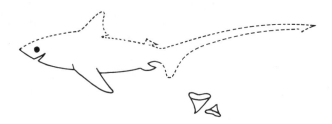

THRESHER:
Upper lobe of tail equal to body.

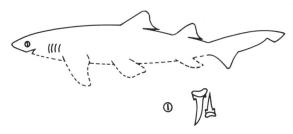

GREY NURSE, RAGGED TOOTH, SAND TIGER:
First and second dorsals almost equal size.
TEETH — long and slender both jaws, with cusps on base.

LEMON SHARKS:
First and second dorsals almost equal size.
TEETH — narrow, slightly serrated at base, no cusps on base.

BASKING SHARK, WHALE SHARK:
Sharks with filter feeding mouths and long gill slits.

NICTITATING MEMBRANE opaque white membrane that slides across eyeball on tigers, blue sharks and other carcharinids and whalers.